'Why did you run out on me?'

'I waited several days, Nicolas, during which time you neither came back, nor wrote, nor sent me even the briefest message of what to expect!' Julia cried accusingly. 'What was I supposed to do?'

'You could have tried a little patience,' Nicolas said harshly. 'You could have trusted me a little.'

'To hell with that, Nicolas! No man is going to keep me on a string like that!'

Dear Reader

Whatever the weather this summer, come with us to four places in the sun. In this collection, we offer you the romance you love—with the Latin lovers of the Mediterranean...the colourful sights and sounds of Spain...the excitement and glamour of Venice...the natural beauty of Greece...the relaxed, timeless magic of France. A wonderful tour of sensual delight, with four happy endings along the way! Something sultry from Mills & Boon...

The Editor

Lee Stafford was born and educated in Sheffield where she worked as a secretary, and later as a public relations assistant. However, she has been a compulsive scribbler for as long as she can remember. She lives in Sussex with her husband, their two teenage daughters and three cats. To keep fit, she swims and does a weekly dance-exercise class. When not travelling to research new backgrounds, she likes to relax at the small apartment they recently bought in France.

WHEN LOVE AWAKES

BY
LEE STAFFORD

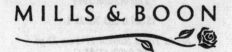

MILLS & BOON

MILLS & BOON LIMITED
ETON HOUSE, 18-24 PARADISE ROAD
RICHMOND, SURREY TW9 1SR

First published in Great Britain 1994 by Mills & Boon Limited

© Lee Stafford 1994

Australian copyright 1994   Philippine copyright 1994 This edition 1994

ISBN 0 263 78521 1

Set in Times Roman 11½ on 12 pt. 86-9407-47131 C

Printed in Great Britain by BPC Paperbacks Ltd A member of The British Printing Company Ltd

CHAPTER ONE

IT WAS cool for July, as it had been all week, and, what was worse, it had started to drizzle as Julia hurried across Dieppe towards the Lestrille building.

She was in none too sweet a mood. The minute Nicolas Lestrille had put down the phone on her, she had tried to call him back to demand an explanation for his abrupt summons, but there had been no answer.

'It is six-thirty,' Anne-Sophie, her French counterpart, had pointed out with irritating reasonableness, her face etched with lines of disapproval, presumably at the chaos which had accompanied Julia into her well-ordered life. 'The offices will be closed, and the switchboard will have shut down for the night.'

'But he rang *me* from there——' Julia blinked, and a mental flashback suddenly showed her Nicolas's antique desk with its battery of phones. He must have a private line, and without knowing that number she could not call him. It was unlisted, of course. Even before she checked in the directory, she knew that it would be.

There was nothing for it but to do as he had so abruptly commanded, and go to his office, much as she detested the idea of taking orders from him. Anne-Sophie had stared blankly at her

5

as she shrugged on her jacket hastily and left the flat. Right at this moment, she hated Nicolas Lestrille more passionately than she had ever hated anyone—even Adam, when she, and not he, had been asked to organise the student exchange, and he had made her choose between accepting the responsibility or continuing their relationship. She had called Adam's bluff and let him go. She could not do that with Nicolas, much as she longed to, because deep down, below her chagrin, she knew that he had not insisted on her immediate presence for the fun of it. If he had called her, then it must concern her.

It must have something to do with the exchange, she thought, breaking into a run across the historic Place de Puits Salé, with one of her students! What if one of them had had an accident, or had been taken seriously ill? Dear God, how could he just ring off like that, without telling her any more? He must know that she would be going frantic with worry!

The office block looked silent and deserted as Julia ran up the steps to the entrance, but even as she reached their seemingly impenetrable barrier the large glass doors slid open, and Nicolas Lestrille stood facing her, a remote-control unit in his hand. He looked grim and drawn, and for once he wasn't in his suit, but more casually attired in trousers and a fine tweed jacket, his shirt tieless and open at the neck.

'What's wrong?' Julia demanded, hurtling full tilt into the reception lobby. 'Why didn't you tell me on the phone what this is all about? Are you trying to send me crazy?'

Her forward momentum was such that she could barely stop herself, and he reached out both hands to arrest her flight, placing them firmly on her shoulders. He still had the remote control in one hand, but it was not the feel of the hard, impersonal black plastic instrument that sent a sudden cold shudder through her, all the way to her knees. She reeled back, staring at him, dark hair wild, blue eyes wide, skin as pale as death, knowing, even through the fog of her anxiety that something violent had happened when he touched her.

'Calm down,' he ordered, a little roughly. 'It's nothing catastrophic, but I needed you here quickly, and I didn't want to explain over the phone when someone else was with you.'

She continued to stare, barely taking in that there was no great disaster, as she had previously suspected there must be, still feeling the raw touch of his hands on her shoulders, even though he had quickly removed them.

Nicolas clicked the remote control again, and the glass doors closed behind them. He pointed Julia towards his private lift, and she entered it like a sleepwalker. It was not a particularly large lift, and it seemed to be full of Nicolas Lestrille, blotting out the moving view of Dieppe which spread out below them as they soared upwards.

'I do wish you'd tell me what is going on!' she cried frustratedly.

'If you give me the chance, I will do so,' he said with strained patience. 'It is the girl—the student you assigned to my company—Kim. She is not feeling too well.'

A frown etched his forehead, and, coming out of her trance of anxiety, Julia realised that he was not simply in a bad mood, or annoyed with her, he was tired—literally fighting fatigue. Despite this, the faint, remembered gleam of fugitive humour lurked in his eyes. How could he find it funny that Kim wasn't well? she thought angrily, her fleeting impulse of sympathy dying on the spot.

The lift reached its destination, and as she stepped into the foyer, Julia saw Kim stretched out full length on one of the couches. Her eyes were closed, and her skin had a peculiar greenish tinge.

'Kim?' she said, dropping to her knees at the side of the supine girl and putting a hand on her forehead. She was not running a temperature—on the contrary, her skin felt cold and clammy as she half opened her eyes and gazed weakly at Julia.

'I'm sorry, Julia...' she muttered thickly. 'I've been s...s...sick...'

Julia looked from Kim up to Nicolas. He seemed very tall and commanding, especially when viewed from this position, but the expression on his face was one of tired irritation rather than anger.

'It's fairly obvious what's wrong, isn't it?' he said, as if Julia were stupid even to require an explanation. 'The plain fact of the matter is that Kim has had a drop too much to drink.'

'Drink?' Julia repeated incredulously. 'Kim? She never drinks anything harder than Coke!'

'Well, today she did, and if she is not used to it maybe that is why it hit her,' he said. 'According to her friend Mark, some of the students met up at lunchtime and celebrated the end of their work experience with varying degrees of enthusiasm.'

'And where is Mark now?' Julia demanded sharply.

'I sent him home when the rest of the staff finished work. There was nothing he could do,' he told her. 'Kim has apparently spent most of the afternoon in the ladies' cloakroom, being rather ill...and being looked after by two of my typists. Very solicitous of them, I'm sure, but they are not short of other work to do.'

Julia groaned, concern for Kim mingled with embarrassment. Of all the people for this to have happened to, Kim, the model student, would have seemed the unlikeliest, and for Nicolas Lestrille to have become involved was Murphy's law at its most malicious.

The recumbent girl began to sob, more from shame, now, than from any great distress.

'I'm sorry!' she wailed. 'I didn't mean to do it...I only had a couple of glasses of wine, and then I started to feel funny...and now I've let you down, Julia...and caused all this bother for Monsieur Lestrille, who's been so kind to me...'

'Hush, don't worry,' Julia comforted her. 'It's not the end of the world, and you'll know better in future.' She glanced up again at the so-kind Monsieur Lestrille, but his face was devoid of readable emotion.

'I thought it best to bring her up here, where she could rest quietly,' he said. 'She will very likely have a monumental headache tomorrow, but all she really needs now is a good night's sleep.'

'I suppose so. Thank you—and I'm sorry you have been put to all this trouble,' she said stiffly. She was glad, now, that he had not gone into detail on the phone, and that she had not been obliged to explain all to the puritanical Anne-Sophie. But had he needed to be quite so brusque?

He shrugged, and the corners of his mouth curled slightly.

'I was on my way out to dinner, would you believe?' he said. 'I got back from Lyon two hours ago, and I only called in the office to check on a few things.'

'Then we shan't inconvenience you any further,' she said promptly. 'If I may use your phone to call a taxi, I'll take Kim back to where she is staying.'

'I have my car outside. I'll run you there,' he said.

She shook her head firmly.

'Oh, no...I mustn't keep you from your dinner date. I can manage,' she protested.

'It isn't exactly a date, just family. They'll wait.' He brushed aside her decisions as if they were drifting leaves. 'And you can't manage. How are you proposing to get Kim down to the lobby? You're hardly built on Amazon proportions, are you?' His all-seeing gaze swept over Julia's slender form, and she felt that strange chill shiver through her once again, like iced water trickling down her back.

Bending over, he picked up Kim as easily as if she were a doll, and Julia could only follow him speechlessly to the lift.

His car was a Mercedes convertible, sleek and white with a black top. Nicolas settled Kim comfortably on the back seat, and opened the front passenger door for Julia.

'You have the address where she is staying?'

She fished in her pocket for her address book, and, fortunately, it was there.

'Here it is. It's at Pourville.'

'A short drive along the coast. I know it.' He headed the car out of town and along the coast road, hands firm and sure on the wheel, driving fast but capably. Julia caught glimpses of green sea flecked with creamy caps of foam between the white cliffs and green velvet fields, and she thought, This isn't happening. He was supposed to be in Lyon, and she should be trying to make polite conversation with Anne-Sophie in her flat.

A sudden thought struck her, and she glanced sharply at Nicolas, who immediately picked up her alarm.

'What is it now?' he demanded, as if he did not quite believe that she could throw any more problems in his direction, when all he wanted to do was to get her off his back and go out to dinner.

She hesitated, but the thought nagged at her, and, whether he was annoyed or not, she could not leave it alone. She had to know.

'Well . . . it's just that . . . you said a group of the students went out for a drink. I was wondering if any of the others got themselves into a similar state to Kim. I really ought to check it out.'

'You can relax. There's no need to worry. I gave young Mark a stiff question-and-answer session before I let him go, and he assured me that no one else was under the weather.'

Julia could well imagine the kind of brisk interrogation Nicolas would have conducted, and it would have taken a strong man rather than a diffident seventeen-year-old boy to fend him off with anything but the truth.

'All the same . . .' she began.

'All the same, it's not done to tell on one's *copains*,' he said. 'I am well aware of the unwritten code of the young, so I didn't take his word for it. I got my private secretary, Etienne, to do a little discreet ringing round the other employers. From the feedback, I gather Mark was being strictly honest.'

She looked at him in astonishment.

'You did all that?'

'If one is going to take on a problem at all, one may as well solve it thoroughly. I'm not a man for half-measures,' he said tersely. 'Now— is this the house?'

They had pulled up outside the neat bungalow where Kim was staying with her French correspondent's family. Julia's throat was dry with apprehension as she wondered how they would react, but she need not have worried. Nicolas lifted Kim from the car, Nicolas carried her to the front door, and it was Nicolas, too, who explained to the French student's mother that the English girl had got herself *'un peu pompette'*. It was done with a casual concern that made no big deal of it, and the woman, plump and sympathetic, was soon agreeing with Nicolas that yes, everyone had done silly things like that at seventeen, clucking and fussing over Kim as if she were her own daughter. She was soon ensconced on the couch with a blanket over her, and Nicolas and Julia were told they were not to worry, the poor girl would be well looked after.

Retracing her steps down the path, Julia found, to her annoyance and mortification, that her legs felt weak, and she was oddly light-headed. Belated relief, because it could obviously have been something far worse, had to be the cause, but it was mingled with a totally unfair resentment of the man at her side, because he had taken over and done the job for her.

'I should have been the one to explain what had happened,' she complained as they reached the car. 'It isn't as if I don't speak the language.'

'You speak it exquisitely, but you are not French, whereas I am, and, with all due respect, I thought it would be accepted more easily if it came from me.' He leaned one arm on the roof of the car, and opened the door for her. 'I was right, I think.'

'Oh, I'm sure you were. I'm sure you always are,' she said sarcastically, swaying a little, suddenly overcome by an immense weariness.

'I suggest you get into the car before you collapse on the spot,' he said coolly.

'I am in no danger of collapsing!' she lied, glaring at him.

'No? You appear fairly stressed to me,' he declared, and his insufferable calm, his refusal to be disturbed, infuriated her all the more.

'Is that any wonder? You phone me up and order me to your office, without giving me any indication of what's wrong!' she all but shouted at him. 'Someone could have broken their neck, or developed acute appendicitis, or...or... whatever!' she finished lamely, the lassitude doubling back on her, dangerously, so that for a terrifying moment she thought she might even pass out.

And then his arm was firm around her waist, guiding her, easing her into the seat, the hard strength and warmth of his hand searing through her jacket and her shirt as if she were not wearing them. As if she were not wearing anything. It was a sensation she could not describe, and it jolted her immediately back into reality. If it was pleasure, there was an element of fear in it, a sense of being taken over. Yet when he slid his arm free and slipped into the driver's seat, she knew a brief but intense moment of deprivation.

'I'm quite all right now,' she said. 'I won't take up any more of your time. If you could just drop me anywhere in Dieppe that's convenient for you...'

He did not answer, but the direction in which he turned the car was clearly not the route back to Dieppe. They were cruising even deeper into the verdant Normandy countryside, past black and white timbered farmhouses, fields of grazing sheep, orchards that were already thick with cider apples, despite the unseasonal nip in the evening air.

'I said I wanted to go back to Dieppe. This isn't the way,' she said sharply.

'It's not a question of what either of us wants. I can't leave you alone in this state,' he said tersely, and she saw the lines of tiredness deepen once again across his forehead. 'You will have to come along with me. It's the only possible solution.'

Julia had rarely, if ever in her life, received such an unwilling invitation. She was imposing on him, and knew it. He didn't want her along, but seemed cursed with a driving need to see everything he embarked upon through to its bitter end. She herself was equally reluctant, but, short of throwing herself from the moving vehicle and limping back to Dieppe, there did not seem to be a reasonable alternative. So she sat tight, hands twisting nervously in her lap, reflecting bitterly

that from the very beginning her relationship with
him had been ill-omened ...

She had had no suspicion that any of these com-
plications would arise when Miss Scott, the head
of modern languages at Merchester College in
Sussex, where she taught, had asked her if she
would organise the French exchange trip. In fact
she had been thrilled and delighted, since it was
only her second year teaching at the college, and
her first job since leaving university.

Determined to make the scheme a success, her
path had none the less been dogged by problems.
To begin with, Adam, the handsome fellow
teacher whom she had been seeing, on and off,
for some months, believed the task should right-
fully have been offered to him, and she was astounded when he suggested that she should
decline it in his favour. Adam considered himself
one hell of a 'catch', but he had seriously mis-
calculated his importance to Julia. Perhaps her
instincts had divined a lack of depths in his
feelings, and she had held back from any serious
commitment to him. In any event, she was not
about to give in to emotional blackmail. Her
career mattered deeply to her, and she was not
there solely to bat out time until some man decided he wanted her to set up house with him!

After all that, she had not been inclined to see
the exchange plans fall to pieces because some
ill-mannered French tycoon—whatever had happened to *toujours la politesse*, for heaven's
sake?—sitting in Dieppe had decided he wanted

nothing to do with it. She had to find French
employers willing to take her students for several
days' work experience in their organisations, and
Lestrille S.A. was a major employer in the area.
But on the one occasion when she had succeeded
in getting through by telephone to the managing
director he had merely growled sardonically that
he was running a business, not a playscheme, and
after that her letters and calls had been in vain.

In a mood of grim determination, she had,
with considerable difficulty, reshuffled her busy
schedule to enable her to take a day off and go
to Dieppe. Surely Nicolas Lestrille could not
refuse her if she appealed to him in person?
Surely no man could be that unreasonable?

But the visit had not even begun auspiciously.
To begin with, she could not find a taxi when
she came down the walkway from the ferry, so
she had been obliged to walk to the Lestrille office
block. Not that it was far, but Dieppe was a seductive town, and she had been waylaid by the
charms of the Grande Rue, pedestrianised and
chock-a-block with fascinating shops, by the historic old buildings clustered around the Eglise St
Jacques, and by the sheer enjoyment of hearing
the spirited flow of French chatter all around her.
Tearing herself away from the enticing window
of a *pâtisserie*, Julia had shaken back her wavy
cloud of raven hair and stepped out briskly, reminding herself that she was not on a pleasure
jaunt; she had a purpose to accomplish. Cutting
through the Parc Jehan Ango, past the town hall,
she had almost been at a trot by the time she

passed the station, and, as a result, when she reached the impressive, slightly intimidating glass and concrete office block of Lestrille S.A. she was slightly breathless.

The image she was anxious to present was that of a coolly pleasant but efficient and determined individual, so she had slowed down consciously as she approached the vast reception desk which was staffed by two impeccably groomed young women.

'Good afternoon,' she said politely in French. 'My name is Julia Delaney, from the Merchester College of Further Education, in Sussex, and I should like to see Monsieur Nicolas Lestrille.'

'You have a *rendezvous, mademoiselle*?' The receptionist, smooth and indomitable, looked her up and down. They must breed them specially, Julia thought wryly.

'No, not exactly—but I *have* come all the way from England specifically for the purpose of seeing him. It concerns the college's French educational exchange, and it is an important project for both communities.'

The receptionist obviously had the French passion for education which her employer appeared to lack, Julia thought, for she looked marginally less immovable.

'In that case, maybe you could speak with his secretary?' she suggested generously.

Maybe she could sing the *Marseillaise* from the ramparts of Dieppe castle, but she did not intend doing so, nor had she rescheduled her day and crossed the Channel to be fobbed off with a secretary! But guile was needed here, and access to the top man's lair was at least a step in the right direction. Julia allowed herself to be directed to a lift, and suppressed a gasp as she realised that it ran up the exterior of the building, its glass-sided column offering her a stupendous birds' eye panorama over the town, the castle on its hill above it, the port and the grey waters of the sea beyond. The lift did not stop—it was evidently a private one, ascending only to the directorial suite on the top floor—and Julia was disgorged into a softly carpeted foyer where a young man, obviously forewarned by reception of her impending arrival, was waiting to greet her.

'Mademoiselle Delaney?'

He was slim and smartly suited, with the look of a college graduate in his first job, and very keen to impress. 'I am Etienne Salmon, Monsieur Lestrille's private secretary. How may I help you?'

A *male* private secretary? Julia had imagined the species to have become extinct in the time of Charles Dickens, and she had expected Nicolas Lestrille's secretary to be a glamorous status-symbol blonde of the kind middle-aged businessmen employed to boost their egos and flatter their male chauvinist tendencies. Nicolas Lestrille must be well endowed with both, in Julia's opinion, or why else had he adamantly refused to discuss with her the work-experience placement of her students in his company?

She smiled winningly at him. Her mouth was generously wide, her teeth white and even, and it was a lovely smile. He gulped, obviously impressed, but Julia warned herself that his boss was not going to be won over by such simple and obvious tactics.

'You can't, Monsieur Salmon, I'm afraid,' she said, apologetic but firm. 'I really do need to talk to Monsieur Lestrille himself, and since neither my letters nor my telephone calls have met with much success I am here in person.'

'But it simply is not possible, *mademoiselle*. Monsieur Lestrille is an extremely busy man.' Etienne Salmon had recovered his aplomb and remembered his priorities. Julia's creamy pale skin with its dusting of freckles over her pert nose, and her deep, black-fringed blue eyes did not pay his salary. 'I am afraid I must ask you to leave, and to write formally requesting an appointment. However, I must warn you that Monsieur Lestrille's diary is heavily booked for some weeks ahead, and...'

'And you can't be overly optimistic,' Julia finished for him, with a grimace scarcely less attractive than her smile. Her blue eyes narrowed, and then began to dance. Two corridors led off from the foyer, but only the *one* lift opened into it...unless there were a helipad on the roof, whoever came into or out of this suite must pass through here...

'Monsieur Salmon,' she suddenly enquired sweetly, 'tell me, is Monsieur Lestrille in his office at the moment?'

'He is not, *mademoiselle*.' The finality in the young man's tone was slightly triumphant, as if he felt he had clinched her defeat, but then, he had not previously had any dealings with Julia, who did not give up that easily!

With a small sigh, she subsided into one of the foyer's luxurious couches, crossing one long leg elegantly over the other. This manoeuvre incidentally hoisted up her skirt an inch higher, and Etienne was still trying not to goggle at her as she said resignedly, 'Oh, well, I shall just have to wait, shan't I? You are expecting him to return, I presume?'

'Yes, but——' He bit his lip, too late to retract the admission. '*Mademoiselle*, you cannot stay here, and you cannot see Monsieur Lestrille without an appointment. It is most irregular, and he will be very much *en colère*.'

Poor lad, he must be scared to death of that old tyrant he works for, Julia thought sympathetically. She saw him glance quickly at a telephone on the wall, wondering, no doubt, if he should call Security. A female secretary would not have hesitated, she was sure, but he did not want either to lose face or to appear ungallant; she was only one young woman, after all, not a full-scale invasion of armed thugs. All the same, Julia's conscience began to nag at her. She did not want to get anyone into trouble...

Just as she was wondering if perhaps she should leave after all, for Etienne's sake, the lift door purred open smoothly, cutting a knife-edge through her indecision, and a man stepped out. Tallish, well-built without being in any sense heavy, exuding a sense of nonchalant strength, his hair not blond exactly, but more a burnished gold, brushed straight back from his brow and breaking into recalcitrant crispness at the nape of his neck. Early thirties, perhaps, Julia guessed; a young executive of the company? But his expression was stern and authoritative as he took in the scene, the agitated secretary and the long-legged, dark-haired girl, obviously engaged in a dispute.

'*Qu'est-ce qui se passe, Etienne?*' he rasped out sharply. 'What's going on here?'

Julia was hard put to stifle a gasp. She had heard that cool, hard voice only once, only briefly, but she recognised it instantly, without Etienne's stammered apology as confirmation.

'I did tell the young lady, Monsieur Lestrille, that you were too busy to see her, and that she could not wait here...' he began.

The other man looked down at Julia, his stare harsh and interrogative, but behind that surface grimness a gleam enlivened his eyes, and she saw he was appraising her, just as she had so recently eyed the cakes in the *pâtisserie*, wondering idly about their relative succulence. He *was* a Frenchman, after all, and maybe it was an inherent reflex, but she did not care for being looked at as if she were a *tarte aux pommes*! Instinctively, she hitched down her skirt, then changing tack altogether, unwound her legs and got to her feet.

'Monsieur Lestrille?' she said, unable to hide the note of query in her voice.

'*Evidemment*,' he said drily, not moving a muscle or giving her the slightest concession. But it was not all that evident to Julia, who had expected the brisk, hard, experienced voice on the phone to belong to a much older man, especially considering the size of the organisation he headed. She risked a smile... it evoked about as much response as powder flung at granite.

'You must not blame Monsieur Salmon for my intrusion,' she said pleasantly. 'It's hardly his fault if he was too polite to have me flung out.'

Nicolas Lestrille's gaze moved only fractionally, but his eyes were now riveted firmly on her face. They were... what...? Not grey, not brown, not amber, but something of all three. What a strange, indefinable man, she thought, wondering at the sharp element of fear that suddenly gripped her. The worst he could do was to call his security men to escort her off the premises. He could hardly toss her down the lift shaft... could he?

'How I apportion blame in my organisation, and for what, is entirely a matter for myself,' he informed her curtly. 'As for you, you have precisely five seconds to tell me who you are and what you think you are doing here.'

'Julia Delaney,' she said promptly and without hesitation. This was not a man you toyed with, and besides, this might be her one and only chance to state her case to him directly. 'I am in charge of the Anglo-French student exchange visit from Merchester College, and I need three more work experience places for my A level students, preferably in your company. I have written, and I have telephoned, all to no avail. You are a hard man to corner, Monsieur Lestrille.'

His eyes held hers, and if that was the suggestion of a smile at the edges of his mouth it was very swiftly suppressed.

'What makes you think you have cornered me, Mademoiselle Delaney?' he demanded ominously.

In view of the hard lines of his mouth, the equally stony glint in his eyes, and his entire immovable, implacable demeanour, it seemed unlikely that this man would have anything remotely resembling a sense of humour. But Julia was a creature of instinct and intuition, and hers were telling her that just maybe he could be reached by that route more easily than by pleading or haranguing, or by adopting a stiff, affronted manner.

'Well, you could give me *dix points* for perseverance,' she said mildly. 'It was extremely choppy in the Channel today, I shall have to spend all night marking essays on Guy de Maupassant when I get home, and who knows what my lower sixth form are subjecting their student teacher to in my absence!'

He didn't laugh, but his mouth relaxed very, very slightly, and Julia felt rather than saw Etienne breathe more easily again.

'I don't know about ten points, but since you are here I will give you ten minutes,' he said crisply, and Julia was slightly winded with surprise, for he had switched to English. 'You had better come into my office. Etienne will rustle up some coffee—or do you insist on tea?'

'Coffee will be fine, thank you,' Julia said weakly. His English was perfectly correct, even idiomatic, but his voice carried the faint trace of Gallic accent that gave his usage of it a distinctive charm. She was not fooled by it for a minute. He could come on sounding like a cross between Charles Aznavour and Gerard Depardieu, but he had the killer instincts of a man-eating shark, she was willing to bet!

CHAPTER TWO

AFTER the luxurious foyer and the ostentatiously
modernist glass lift, Julia expected Nicolas
Lestrille's office to be vast, palatial, and fur-
nished with a black ash desk, white leather
couches, and floor-to-ceiling entertainment cabi-
nets. Contrarily, it was modest in size and looked
more like the office of a provincial lawyer, with
a large antique oak desk, venerable chairs, and
a glass-fronted cupboard bursting with books.
He doesn't fit, was her sudden, unconnected
thought; he just isn't all of a piece. Why not?

But she had been promised ten minutes, and
could not afford to waste time pondering. Etienne
brought in coffee in a glass and chrome cafetière,
and Julia launched herself without preamble.

'I teach in the modern languages department
of Merchester College, and I have been given the
responsibility of arranging the exchange visit. As
you probably know, this involves English A level
students coming over here and living *en famille*
with French counterparts for a week.'

'Yes, Miss Delaney, I am conversant with the
mechanics of how a student exchange works,'
he said. 'At a later date, the French students
go to England, where the process is reversed. Is
that correct?'

The coffee tray stood on the desk between them. He picked up the cafetière and poured coffee into the cups. 'Black or white?'

'Black, please,' said Julia, whose stomach was still recovering from a fairly rough sea crossing. She watched the steady progress of his hand, long, surprisingly sensitive-looking fingers which made one think he might play the piano. How silly to think any such thing. He most certainly had no time for anything but making money...

She forced her mind back to the matter in hand, and pressed on.

'As part of the project, we expect the students to spend part of the week working in a local business here in and around Dieppe.'

'*D'accord.*' A note of edgy weariness had crept into his voice. 'There are many who would be only too happy to oblige you. Why choose me, Miss Delaney? I am a very busy man.'

Julia opened her briefcase and took out the folder of exchange details which she had brought with her.

'As you will see from this, many companies, banks and other enterprises have indeed been most co-operative,' she said, and without her having intended it, her own voice took on a faintly accusatory note. 'But Lestrille S.A. is a large organisation...a major employer. To put it plainly, I was relying on you to take some of my students.'

'The folly of relying on someone you don't know, with no reason for belief other than your own wish to have things so, is a typically feminine delusion, I find,' he said softly, almost tauntingly. 'You can hardly hold me responsible if I fail to go along with it.'

Julia tossed back her head, setting the dark waves of her hair flying angrily before they settled back once more on her shoulders.

'It is nothing of the kind, and I resent that accusation! It is a reasonable assumption that a prestigious company, with roots in a community, would be keen to participate in an educational project!' she exclaimed, a black, black rage she knew all too well as part of her own temperament boiling up within her. 'I would have thought that merely as a public relations exercise the benefits would be obvious to a businessman reputedly as astute as yourself!'

'You do a nice mixture of flattery and condemnation, Miss Delaney,' Nicolas Lestrille said with distinct amusement. 'Someone once said that "patriotism is the last refuge of a scoundrel". Nowadays it is public relations which occupies that slot. I don't *need* such dubious assistance. I am already well known locally. I do my sums correctly, treat my staff fairly, market whatever I sell properly, and my interest is in increasing my turnover and keeping local people in full employment. That's my business, and I don't have time to waste on frills. *Entendu*?'

The black rage had smouldered to a red-hot barbecue in Julia's breast, and now she knew, from bitter past experience that she would no longer be capable of tamping it down.

'Frills!' she exclaimed indignantly, jumping up and knocking over her coffee, so that a thin brown stream spread over the polished surface of the desk. 'Is that the contempt with which you treat the new Europe, the new spirit of co-operation and friendship? These students are not coming here simply to improve their verb conjugations, *monsieur*! They will be forging links that will take us ahead into the future with a greater understanding of each other. But if that is not important to you, well—*tant pis*! I'll manage without your help. In fact, I'll be better off without it!'

Snatching up her briefcase, she turned and made for the door in what she hoped was a dignified stalk, but feared was more of a furious stumble.

Her hand was on the doorknob when he said quietly, 'Miss Delaney?'

There was no anger or any other discernible emotion in his voice, but the very calmness of it acted like a muffler to her own outburst of temper. Slowly, unwillingly, she turned, to find him still seated in the same position behind his desk, apparently unmoved by the storm she had unleashed.

'Sit down again,' he said with quiet authority, and she recognised the approach she herself used if she had a difficult student in her class. Recognised and resented it. How could she have allowed herself to boil over like that? But then, how could she have prevented it?

'Why should I?' she demanded sullenly.

'Because, for one thing, I still have your folder here,' he said reasonably, and, feeling incredibly foolish for having left it behind in her anger, Julia retraced her steps and slid back into her chair.

Nicolas Lestrille opened a drawer of his desk, took out a wad of tissues, and efficiently mopped up the spilt coffee. Then he calmly refilled Julia's cup. Finally, he snapped open a spectacle case and put on a pair of gold-rimmed reading glasses. They made him look sternly intellectual, like a powerful academic. He read through Julia's carefully planned exchange details without a word, while she sat there, too emotionally depleted and apprehensive of what he might do next, to say anything at all.

When he had finished—he was obviously a quick reader, and it did not take him long—he took off the spectacles again and pushed the folder back across the desk towards her.

'I will agree to take two of your students at Lestrille S.A.,' he said coolly and formally. 'But do not imagine for a minute that your impassioned little performance influenced my decision, rather than the obviously meticulous nature of your planning. Logic, Miss Delaney, impresses me, where business is concerned, emotionalism not at all. As a matter of fact, I did not think the English went in much for the latter.'

Julia found her voice at last.

'Ah, but I'm half Irish,' she told him. 'And while I'm sure you won't regret your decision, I do have three more students to place. Why don't you agree to take all of them?'

Nicolas Lestrille leaned back in his chair, and there was a dangerous glimmer in his eyes.

'Quit while you are ahead, Miss Delaney, if you have any sense at all,' he drawled sardonically. 'I said *two* students, and furthermore those you send me had better be industrious and prepared to give one hundred and ten per cent. I have no room for timewasters in this organisation.'

He pressed a buzzer on his desk, and Etienne appeared in the doorway like the genie of the lamp, to escort her out. Julia was left in no doubt that she had been dealt with and summarily dismissed.

She caught the five-thirty ferry from Dieppe and simmered quietly all the way back across the Channel to Newhaven. Her annoyance did not abate as she drove home through the dripping Sussex countryside to the ancient town of Merchester, where she lived in a tiny house snuggled up against the walls of the ruined Norman castle.

Her mission had been successful, in that she had placed two students with Lestrille S.A. However, Julia did not feel as if this were something she had personally achieved, for all her efforts. Nicolas Lestrille, for arbitrary, capricious or just plain cussed reasons of his own, had decided to agree to take part in the scheme, and only after having taken great pleasure in making her jump through several kinds of hoop for her reward.

To begin with, he had made her go through the performance of explaining the scheme to him—as she had already done very fully in her letters, which had received only perfunctory and non-committal replies. Then he had mockingly implied that she was no more than a silly female who had assumed that she would naturally get her own way. Not surprisingly, this had goaded her into losing her temper, as he must have fully expected it to do, despite his comments on English sang-froid, and she had obligingly leapt for the bait, to his great amusement.

She had left a man in order to push through this exchange. Admittedly, after the petulant way Adam had behaved, she had realised he really wasn't worth losing her cool over, and she had begun to wonder what she had ever seen in him. But the same instincts which told her this truth were also warning her that the adversary with whom she had crossed swords in Dieppe was far more formidable. He was both detestable and dangerous, and it was no use consoling herself that now she had got her students in his company she would have nothing more to do with him. She was afraid it would not work out that way. There would inevitably be contact. She would have to deal with him, to face the challenge of his arrogant manner, his grim, wrong-footing humour. Like it or not, it could hardly be avoided.

*   *   *

It had seemed little short of a miracle to Julia that the arrangements for the exchange had finally come together, that every student had a work-experience placement awaiting him or her, and that she finally managed to get twenty assorted seventeen-year-olds on to the cross-Channel ferry. Chrissie, the young student teacher she had brought along to help her, was harassed and uncertain, and Julia could only hope she would gain in confidence as the week progressed. She needed the experience, and two members of staff were necessary on an exchange. Who knew whether someone would be taken ill, or have to be escorted home? In which case one of them would have to be released for that duty. However, it had been difficult, initially, to see Chrissie as a source of support rather than another dependant.

As the ship had steamed into the sheltered *avant-port* of Dieppe harbour, and she had gazed down at the tall grey houses and lively cafés ringing the quayside, Julia had had to admit to a certain apprehension herself. She wanted so passionately for this venture to be a success, and at this point she had been able to envisage any number of things that could go wrong and prevent that success from being achieved.

The teacher in charge of the French side of the exchange was a greying, pleasant-looking man in his fifties, called Olivier Gérard, whom Julia immediately found sympathetic. Chrissie would be staying with him and his wife, and Julia was sure she would be well looked after. She was less sanguine about the arrangements which had been made for her. She was to stay at the flat of Olivier's assistant, Anne-Sophie Duval, and it had instantly been apparent to Julia that she and Anne-Sophie were not destined to be soulmates.

The French teacher was about thirty, quiet and reserved, everything about her appearance and her manner neat and controlled. Julia's own emotions tended to be close to the surface and easily stirred, but Anne-Sophie looked as if she gave little away. She wore a more or less constant air of disapproval, which Julia had soon found directed at her.

'You allow your students to address you by your first name?' she had asked, with prim incredulity. 'I am not sure that is *comme il faut*.'

Julia had smiled. Miss Scott had had her doubts about that approach, too, although, to give her her due, she had allowed Julia to do things her own way.

'I'm less than ten years older than they are, and they are already young adults,' she had replied easily. 'If holding their respect depends on being called "Miss Delaney", I'm not much of a teacher.'

Anne-Sophie had not laughed, and Julia doubted that she had much of a sense of humour. For herself, however serious things were, there was often an under-swell of fun bubbling below the surface and occasionally breaking through at inconvenient moments, and she had found that her humorous tendencies had to be kept well under control during the week that followed.

The French girl lived in a first-floor flat above a shop on a street just off the Grande Rue. She was tidy to the point of obsessiveness, and everything was so spick and span that Julia felt she dared not leave so much as a magazine lying around. While she was polite and careful of her guest's needs, Anne-Sophie was also deadly serious, and lived her life with a planned purposefulness which left no room for impulse. It was, as Julia had feared it would be, hard going. After a weekend of this, she had almost looked forward to the break in monotony of taking Mark and Kim, the two students she had assigned to Lestrille S.A., along to their place of employment.

Almost—but not quite. She had divided the task of introducing the young people to their employers between herself and Chrissie, and although she had been sorely tempted she had been obliged to admit that sending Chrissie along to see Nicolas Lestrille was tantamount to throwing Christians to the lions. This was one she had to handle herself.

But even the intimidating receptionists on the desk were suitably deferential and welcoming that morning, and the three of them had been swiftly ushered into the private lift and whisked upstairs to the managerial quarters.

'Monsieur Lestrille can be a little... brusque...but don't let it worry you unduly,' she warned her young charges. 'I'm sure you'll be fine so long as you work hard and do as you are asked. His private secretary, Etienne, is young and very pleasant, and will probably look after you.'

But when they stepped out of the lift into the foyer it was not Etienne but a middle-aged woman who greeted them, introducing herself as Madame Dubuis, Monsieur Lestrille's secretary.

An awful suspicion, which had once flitted half jestingly through Julia's mind, began to grow uncomfortably. He couldn't have! He just couldn't—not even Nicolas Lestrille could be that severe, that vindictive!

As he emerged from his office suite, she all but pounced on him, quite forgetting for the moment who he was, and why she was here.

'What's happened to Etienne! You've fired him, haven't you?' she accused fiercely. 'How could you do that? I told you that it wasn't his fault that I refused to leave——'

Her hands were clenched, her eyes blazing blue sparks, her entire stance was combative, and Nicolas Lestrille, dark-suited and immaculate, looked down at her with an expression that was slightly annoyed, but also genuinely puzzled. Mark and Kim were gazing at her with mouths agape—they had never seen their teacher this angry before, for all she had a reputation for a quick Irish temper—and it was perhaps fortunate that their French was not quite good enough yet to understand the rapid flow of hers.

'Fired Etienne? What *are* you talking about?' Nicolas demanded. 'Why on earth should I do that?'

Julia stared back at him, trying to decide whether or not he was bluffing. If he were not, then she had just behaved with incredible foolishness.

'Because . . . because of what happened the day I came to see you . . .' she stammered, and an amused understanding began to dawn in his strange eyes.

'Etienne,' he said patiently, condescendingly, 'is away on a course. He will be back tomorrow. Madame Dubuis is merely standing in for him.' He sighed. 'I do not know where you get hold of these macabre ideas, Mademoiselle Delaney. It must be your Celtic imagination. However, I am not Genghis Khan, nor the Emperor Caligula. There are no dungeons below Lestrille S.A. to which hapless transgressors disappear, never to be seen again. Please remember that. I may have a reputation to maintain, but it's not that bad, I do assure you.'

Julia wished she could have hurled herself back into the lift and descended to the ground floor in the wink of an eye. Anything, rather than having to stand here and face the results of her own impulsive stupidity.

'There's no need to be facetious,' she said, with low-voiced embarrassment. 'I didn't——'

'Didn't think before you spoke?' he suggested pointedly. 'Do try it some time—if only for your own sake.'

Leaving her still fuming, he turned to the two students, with an outstretched hand and a smile so charming that it made her words of warning

in the lift seem as unnecessary as her recent
outburst.

'Welcome to Lestrille S.A., Mark and Kim,'
he said, speaking in French, but more slowly and
clearly for their benefit. 'I hope you will enjoy
your brief stay with us. If you go along now with
Madame Dubuis, she will show you where you
are to work, and I expect I shall see you at some
time during your visit.'

Julia knew that it was not her place to go with
her students any further at this point, and
therefore she had no option be to remain alone
with Nicolas. She regarded him warily, hoping
that the pink flush had faded from her skin, and
that it had returned to its normal creamy pallor.
She was still uneasy and on her guard, whereas
he looked as relaxed and omnipotent as a lion in
a field of wildebeest, whose only decision was to
choose the precise moment to pounce and devour.

'Just one point, Miss Delaney,' he said
smoothly. 'You forwarded me the information
regarding the two students, but you unfortunately omitted to mention one small detail—that
Kim is a girl.'

Julia's eyes snapped into battle again.

'So?' she challenged. 'Kim is short for
Kimberley.'

'As I discovered, when I checked with Olivier
Gérard,' he said. 'I had not come across it before.
French names usually make the owner's sex
obvious, you see. Jean—Jeanne, François,
Françoise. English, on the other hand, is rife
with ambiguities.'

'I see all that. What I fail to understand is why it is important,' Julia said stubbornly. 'Kim is a very bright girl who wants to do French and business studies at university after taking her A levels. I must insist that she be given exactly the same treatment as Mark. I don't want her relegated to making the coffee!'

He grinned, much to Julia's fury.

'My dear *mademoiselle*, surely you are not insinuating that Lestrille S.A. is not an equal opportunities employer?' he said softly. 'After all, it must be fairly obvious that I didn't employ Etienne for his legs!'

Even as he spoke, he glanced down obliquely at hers, and even though her skirt stopped short only at her knees Julia suffered a bruising sensation of being exposed. Worse—it was as if he had slid his hand over the skin of her thigh, fully expecting his invasive touch to be enjoyed. She told herself that this was ridiculous, that he had not laid a finger on her, and was unlikely to, but it did not help.

'So what difference does it make that Kim is a girl?' she demanded.

'Whatever your feminist principles, Miss Delaney, you have to admit that there are different arrangements to be made in the workplace for difference sexes,' he said patronisingly. 'There is the use of cloakroom lockers, and the like. Also, it affects the matter of where we decide to give her space. She may not like to be in a drawing office with twenty young men. Or she may like it very much, but it would not be exactly ideal.'

Julia was momentarily taken aback by the plain logic of his argument, but she was not about to concede.

'Kim is a very shy, well brought up girl. She's not forward at all,' she said defensively.

'I can see that for myself. It is fortunate for her that I assumed it would be the case, is it not?' he said.

He raised his hand, and for a moment she thought he was going to rest it on her shoulder. All her muscles tensed in anticipation, but he was merely glancing at his watch.

'A word of advice, *mademoiselle*,' he said, his voice still hovering on the edge of laughter. 'You have a fine fighting spirit. Don't waste it fighting unnecessary battles.'

'When I feel I have need of your advice, *monsieur*,' she replied frostily, 'I will ask for it. A lot of time may pass in the interim, so in the meantime I will just wish you *au revoir*.'

She turned her back on him deliberately and pressed the button to call the lift. She seemed to be waiting an eternity for it, feeling his eyes boring into her stiff back, although she knew that it could only have been moments. Just before getting into it, she could not resist a swift glance over her shoulder.

He wasn't there. She had never heard him go back into his office, but he had not even troubled to wait, and that feeling she had had of being watched by him was only an illusion.

She was in such a foul mood when she returned to the flat that even Anne-Sophie noticed and was moved to ask if she had a problem.

'Nicolas Lestrille!' she said, as if the mere words were sufficient explanation in themselves. 'That man is the last word in arrogance! Do you know him?' she added more cautiously.

But the French girl merely raised her shoulders in a shrug.

'I am acquainted with him, of course. Everyone knows who he is. He's a prominent member of the community,' she said. 'But there would be little point in your trying to get to know him any better. I should not think there are many who can really say that they do.'

'I wouldn't want to,' Julia said fervently. 'Presumably his wife loves him!'

She was aware that she was fishing, and rather despised herself for seeking information in such a trite manner, but Anne-Sophie responded swiftly.

'*Mon Dieu*, Nicolas is not married,' she said firmly. 'He has not had the time for such trivia as looking for a wife, although there are any number who fool themselves they are eligible. After all, he is rich, good-looking, powerful. But he has devoted every minute of the last twelve years to building up Lestrille S.A. His only goal has been success.'

'I can well believe it of him,' Julia said. 'What a one-sided existence his must be. Everyone needs a personal life...friends...pastimes...however hard and dedicatedly they work, however ambitious they are. Such single-mindedness isn't natural.'

'It is for Nicolas. He is different from other men,' Anne-Sophie insisted firmly, and her tone was almost admiring. 'His friends are all business contacts, and work is his hobby. That is not to say there are never women in his life. One sees him around with them from time to time, of course, but never with the same one very often. They say that there is a queue.'

Julia made a little moue of disgust. What kind of woman would wait in line for her chance to go out on a few dates with a work-obsessed man to whom she was no more than a decorative sex-object, knowing that he would quickly move on before she got any foolish ideas about a deeper involvement?

'I can't imagine women still exist who will put up with that kind of treatment,' she said, half joking. 'As for anyone wanting to marry him— they would have to be one sandwich short of a picnic!'

Anne-Sophie was unamused, her lips compressed primly, and she regarded Julia sternly, as if she found her attitude altogether too frivolous.

'Frenchwomen see these things rather differently,' she said reprovingly.

At this, Julia laughed out loud.

'Oh, come on, Anne-Sophie!' she exclaimed, unable to go along with this, even for the sake of domestic peace between them. 'I'm sorry, but I just don't believe you. *You* wouldn't hang around after a man like that, however rich, powerful, handsome, et cetera, et cetera, he happened to be! Would you?'

Anne-Sophie pursed her lips in severe disapproval.

'I am a career woman,' she pointed out prissily. 'It is not necessary for such as I am to behave as if marriage were my only goal. I would have thought that was self-evident.'

'Of course,' Julia murmured, thoroughly alarmed at the storm of self-righteousness she had unwittingly whipped up. 'Excuse me, I—er—I have some shopping to do...'

She fled, swiftly, to the refuge of the old Café des Tribunaux, with its comfortable green leather banquettes and smoky atmosphere, a place where half of Dieppe seemed to meet. There was only so much of Anne-Sophie she could take at a time!

The following day, a reception was held at the Town Hall for the students, English and French, their employers, and everyone concerned with the exchange. Various dignitaries from the town made welcoming speeches. A buffet lunch was set out, preceded by drinks—nothing stronger than wine, besides the Coke and fruit juices, in view of the youth of the participants.

Glass in hand, Julia circulated, talking to the bank manager, the tour operator, the assistant supermarket manager, and the estate agent, all of whom were affable and enthusiastic about their part in the exchange. She was in the middle of a comparison of English and French conveyancing practice with the latter, when Olivier Gérard tapped her gently on the shoulder.

And turning, Julia found herself looking straight into the eyes of Nicolas Lestrille.

He must have only just arrived, for somehow she was sure that if he had been in the room earlier she would have been aware of him. He was not the sort of man whose presence could be missed. Coldly overbearing, maybe. Unobtrusive, never. If he were there he would be seen, known, remarked upon.

'Monsieur Lestrille,' she said, her voice calm, her mind annoyingly far from matching it. 'How good of you to find the time to come, when one knows how busy you always are.'

'Ah, you two have already met, then?' Olivier said. 'Then you do not need me as an intermediary.' He drifted away, leaving them oddly alone in the crowd.

'So, Miss Delaney,' Nicolas said, looking down at her with a cool, unfathomable gaze. 'You must be feeling gratified, at this point, that you have succeeded in getting your exchange up and running.'

'Thanks to all the help I have been given,' she replied smoothly. 'Including—ultimately, if a little reluctantly—your own.'

A flicker of response stirred in his eyes. They were grey, she decided. But no—wait. An amber gleam swirled in the dark irises, lightening them suddenly. His suit today was of a pale coffee colour; he looked groomed, professional, businesslike. The perfect entrepreneurial machine. Only—the way his hair decided to curl rebelliously into the nape of his neck, as if he had just been swimming and damp-towelled it, made a contradictory footnote to all that suave, crisp perfection. Her eyes followed the line of the small pearl buttons fastening his immaculate ivory shirt, to the silk tie knotted just so at his throat, before she forcibly tore herself away from such minute inspection.

'Are you still wondering,' he said, poker-faced, 'if, after all, I am a fit person to have charge of your impressionable young protégés for a whole week?'

'*Comment*? What?' Julia could not suppress her startled exclamation, and her eyes met his again, full on.

'I must assume that was the reason for your in-depth deliberation,' he went on, and damn it, she really could not tell if he were perfectly serious or subtly teasing. 'You were scrutinising me as if I were an examination paper you were marking, and had not quite decided if it deserved to pass or fail.'

'Oh, really!' she protested, dissembling madly. 'I was doing no such thing! You are being far too imaginative, Monsieur Lestrille.'

His laugh was a short rasp.

'Imaginative? No, Miss Delaney, that is not a charge you can level at me,' he stated firmly. 'But you need not feel too concerned. Even if you are convinced that I eat English students for breakfast instead of *petits pains*, Mark and Kim are unlikely to see much of me.'

Julia was fighting off a growing irritation which had its roots in a deeper embarrassment. He had observed her close inspection of him, and, while he had pretended to find a reason for it, she wondered what he really thought. That she was admiring his elegant turn-out... or, worse, his fine physique, his undeniable if unconventional good looks, succumbing to his strange, abrasive charm? For heaven's sake, thought Julia, thoroughly alarmed, that would not do. She had to fight back properly, and sarcasm was the most immediate weapon she could find to hand.

'Of course not, Monsieur Lestrille,' she said sweetly. 'I do realise that you are far too exalted a personage to bother yourself with such trivialities.'

He laughed again, with low, scathing, triumphant amusement.

'Trivial or not, I do not have the power to be in two places at one time,' he told her, 'and it so happens that for much of the coming week I shall be in Lyon, on a trip for which the arrangements were made some months ago. Business, naturally.' He smiled, an expression of almost Byzantine complexity, making her feel like a novice who had dared, unwisely, to challenge a grand master in the art of cut and thrust. 'However, I am sure that my absence will not affect the success of the exchange, and I wish you *bonne chance*, *mademoiselle*. And now it is my turn to wish you *au revoir*.'

'But...aren't you staying for lunch?' Julia heard herself asking, for all the world as if his departure would cast a blight over the occasion.

'*Malheureusement, non*. I only had the time to look in for a moment, since I have a lunch appointment. Business again.'

'Naturally,' said Julia.

The look he bestowed on her then did something weird and quite unprecedented to a spot at the base of Julia's spine. He did not exactly smile, but his mouth relaxed slightly, and his eyes, in that moment, were definitely brown. There is no point in your behaving antagonistically towards me, his expression said, because you are, after all, only a woman, and I have the measure of you. I shan't take you seriously, but if I wanted to manipulate you I could all too easily do so.

'I do hope I have not disappointed you,' he said.

'Absolutely not,' she riposted stonily. '*Au contraire*, Monsieur Lestrille.'

She watched him leave the hall, anger beating a sharp tattoo along her nerves. What was it that he had been trying to tell her by means of hint and innuendo and glance? That he hadn't really the time or the interest, but if he had, and he wanted to, he could have her eating out of his hand? Of all the conceited, cocksure, self-centred...Julia was fast running out of enough adjectives to describe him, although she could think of a few more graphic ones she had heard emanating from the upper sixth common-room from time to time!

As she went in to lunch, she thought furiously that she would love to take him down a peg or two! And then she remembered his words. He was going away, to Lyon. They very probably would not have occasion to meet again.

A good job too, Julia muttered under her breath. And she tried not to wonder why some of the excitement had gone out of the prospect of the week ahead.

CHAPTER THREE

ALL in all, Julia congratulated herself cautiously as the week progressed, things were going rather well. After an initial period of perfectly natural shyness, all her students seemed to be getting on with their French opposite numbers, and had begun to communicate more confidently in French. In some cases, she could even discern the roots of what might turn out to be lasting friendships.

The only problems which had arisen had been minor ones, well within her capacity to solve: brief attacks of homesickness, or slight misunderstandings concerning the work experience. She visited all the participating employers to reassure herself that all was proceeding smoothly, including Lestrille S.A. This was a far less intimidating prospect armed with the knowledge that Nicolas was elsewhere, and that she would not be obliged to confront him, since every time they met she seemed to end up getting the worst of the encounter.

But she was welcomed pleasantly by Etienne, newly returned from his course, and looking spruce and efficient. He was due for a promotion soon, he told her enthusiastically. Not that he did not enjoy working directly with Monsieur Lestrille—on the contrary, he had learned a lot

49

from his example—but it was good to have one's efforts rewarded by advancement, was it not?

Indeed it was, Julia agreed sagely.

'I understand that Monsieur Lestrille is in Lyon at the moment,' she remarked, just to make sure that he had not changed his mind, and might unexpectedly appear and throw her off balance once again.

'That is so, but we do not allow ourselves to take things easy in his absence, I can assure you,' Etienne said. 'He likes to know what is going on here, wherever he happens to be. In fact, he has telephoned several times to check on the progress of the English students. He is very concerned that they should profit from their time here.'

'I'm pleased to hear it,' Julia said, glad that she had seen fit to send her two brightest students to Lestrille S.A. 'Both Mark and Kim seem to have found their work here interesting, so please convey my thanks to Monsieur Lestrille when he gets back. I shall write to him formally, of course, to do the same.'

And that was obviously the truth. She would say 'thank you for taking part in the scheme, and for having my students, who found the experience worthwhile and valuable'. The polite, standard letter of appreciation which she would send out to everyone concerned.

Where Nicolas Lestrille was concerned, it somehow did not seem sufficient. There was so much more she wanted to say. She would have liked to ask, for instance, why he had been so reluctant, initially, and why he had changed his mind. Was he really a man for whom nothing seriously existed outside business, or was there another Nicolas buried deep within that persona? What forces had motivated him to devote himself so single-mindedly to the development of his rapidly expanding organisation, to the exclusion of his needs as a human being...as a man?

It seemed to her that in their brief meetings, here in his office, and at the reception, she had embarked on a dialogue with him, and, while she could not say that she liked him, she had to admit that he intrigued her, and refused to be banished from her thoughts.

But a dialogue took two. She might have questions, but he was not of a mind to provide her with answers. He had cut her off, dismissed her, made it clear on every occasion that he had no time to spare and nothing to say to her. Awful man! Since she would not be seeing him again, she would put him out of her mind, Julia resolved firmly, striding out of the glass and concrete offices.

Thursday arrived, the students' final day at their various places of work. Friday had been designated a free day, and Julia had planned to take them all on a trip to the historic city of Rouen. Surely, nothing could go wrong now, she thought, taking a deep breath and beginning to relax, but the thought was premature.

She had been out doing a little personal shopping that afternoon—presents to take back, mementos of the trip, and so on—and, arriving back at Anne-Sophie's flat, she quickly took her

purchases into the guest bedroom she was occupying. Her hostess did not like clutter, and was
already looking askance at Julia's plastic carrier
bags and packages.

While she was stowing them neatly away, she
heard the telephone ring in the living-room, but
did not take much notice, not expecting the call
to be for her. Then Anne-Sophie tapped on her
door.

'It is for you,' she said as Julia emerged, and
there was a strange, curious look on her face. 'It
is Nicolas Lestrille.'

'It can't be!' Julia said at once. 'He is out of
town.' Her nerves felt suddenly strung-out and
finely stretched. She could not escape him.

'I assure you that it is he,' Anne-Sophie said
a little curtly, and she continued to watch Julia
quite openly as she picked up the receiver.

'Monsieur Lestrille,' she said, as coolly as she
could. 'It is good of you to take the trouble to
telephone me long distance, but I have seen for
myself, and Etienne has confirmed that all has
gone well with the two students I sent to Lestrille
S.A.'

'Don't be ridiculous, Miss Delaney!' he barked
coldly. 'Why would I phone you from Lyon? I
am right here, in my office in Dieppe, and I want
you over here immediately. *Toute de suite*!'

Julia gasped audibly. Who did he think he was,
talking to her in that manner, summoning her so
peremptorily? Even if he had the right to give her
orders—which he did not, since she was not one

of his employees—he had no business addressing her with such brusque arrogance.

'Just a minute!' she said angrily. 'You can't talk to me that way! I should like to know what all this is about before I come chasing across Dieppe at your say-so. I am not one of your slaving hundreds!'

He treated this protest with the supreme contempt of utter indifference.

'*Toute de suite*! Five minutes at the outside,' he repeated coldly, and, without a word of explanation, rang off, leaving her staring at the receiver, her face a picture of complete stupefaction.

A chapter of errors, Julia thought now, reflecting on the events which had brought her to this point, sitting in Nicolas Lestrille's car, as he drove smoothly along the country lanes, taking her...where, she did not know, and with no great pleasure. She cast a swift glance at his sternly set face, and tried again to persuade him that this course of action was not necessary.

'I really am perfectly all right, now,' she assured him. 'I am perfectly capable of taking care of myself.'

'Had you plans for the evening?' His voice was cool and formal.

'No, nothing definite. I thought I might phone Chrissie, my assistant, and suggest dinner at a restaurant, but...'

'Look,' he said, a touch wearily, and with an underlying note of impatience, 'if you go back

now to where you are staying, you're going to
have to answer questions about this episode.
Now, I don't know how well you get on with your
hostess, or how much you trust her discretion…'

He left the sentence unfinished, and Julia
glanced sharply at him.

'Do you know Anne-Sophie Duval?'

'Only slightly,' he said. 'But you have to admit,
the less this story gets around, the better it would
be, both for Kim and for yourself. While no one
could expect you to chaperon a group of seventeen-year-olds for every minute of their stay,
whatever they do is bound to reflect on you, fairly
or otherwise, wouldn't you agree?'

She sighed. Apart from scaring her half out of
her wits, he appeared to have worked it all out
and handled it very competently.

'I suppose so,' she agreed.

'Then absent yourself for a couple of hours,
and let it all blow over,' he suggested, and Julia
had to admit that the prospect of returning to
Anne-Sophie's flat and either explaining, or
trying to avoid explaining, what had taken place
to the French girl, who already disapproved of
her, was not appealing. She had honestly tried
her best, during the week, but there was no great
warmth in Anne-Sophie, and the time they had
been obliged to spend in each other's company
had been, frankly, a bit of a strain. Nicolas could
not know that, though, could he? It was a little
frightening what he did seem to know, or to work
out for himself by some mysteriously efficient
inner process.

'Besides,' he added, with the ghost of a grin, 'I am already late for dinner.'

'But where precisely are we going?' Julia demanded, still unable to escape the growing certainty that she had become a definite liability to him.

'To my uncle's home,' he said shortly.

'But they won't be expecting me,' she protested worriedly. 'I mean, they won't have catered for me either. Won't it make things awkward for them if you turn up with someone else, when they thought you would be alone?'

'Not in the least,' he said, his voice hard. 'It isn't that sort of a household. Don't worry. I am quite entitled to invite anyone I please.'

That was rather a strange way to speak in relation to the members of one's family, and it made Julia more reluctant than ever to go along with him.

'Maybe,' she said, 'but you would presumably do them the courtesy of informing them in advance. And besides, if I am going out to dinner, I dress accordingly, whereas right now, I look a mess. I've been in this suit since morning, and I haven't even had the chance to wash my face and put on some fresh make-up!'

'Your hair could use a comb,' he agreed imperturbably, and she shot him an affronted glare. No man was supposed to react like that. 'You look fine,' was the standard response. Obviously, it was futile expecting anything standard from Nicolas Lestrille. Pulling down the mirror above her window, she ran her fingers through

her tousled black locks. She did not even have
her handbag with her, so there was little more
she could do to make herself presentable.

But then she forgot all about her appearance,
as he turned off the winding lane they had been
following, and between large double gates to a
private road lined with huge, stately elms. At the
end of the road, Julia saw a house—no, she did
not see a house! Correction—what she saw was
a château. A Renaissance château, constructed
at around the same time the kings and noblemen
of France were building their famous châteaux
in the Loire valley, to allow them to escape the
summer heat of Paris, to hunt wild game, plot
intrigues, and dally with their mistresses.

Two long, parallel rows of windows flanked
an impressive entrance, with curved flights of
steps approaching it from either side. In front of
this, formal gardens were laid out, with balus-
trades and statuary, and an elegant fountain with
nymphs and cupids holding the basin aloft, and
stone dolphins cavorting in the gently splashing
water. The rain had died away now, and a watery
evening sun cast a romantic glow over the scene,
so that for a moment Julia felt she had been
transported back to another age, and half expected ladies in flowing dresses to drift across the
parterres and terraces.

'What *is* this place?' she gasped.

The smile he turned on her as he parked the
car was heavy with unexplained irony.

'My uncle's home, as I told you,' he said. 'Shall
we go in? Oh—and it might look better if you

called me Nicolas and I called you Julia, don't you think?'

She sat for a moment, nonplussed, looking back at him, but his face gave nothing away.

'Would you like me to address you as "*tu*" as well?' she asked sardonically.

'No, that might be going to far,' he said amusedly. 'Calling someone by their first name is one thing. Using the familiar form of address, that's quite another. We don't want them to run away with the idea that we are fairly intimately acquainted, do we?'

'I think it's highly unlikely that they would,' she retorted crisply, getting out of the car and smoothing down her skirt. But her creamy pale skin felt hot and pink at the mere idea, and she found herself recalling, unwillingly but with great precision, the hard touch of his hands on her shoulders, the warmth of his arm around her waist, and wondering what it would be like really to be touched by him. Intentionally, sexually. Her breasts tightened and her legs weakened again, and she reminded herself that this was a man she hardly knew, and was not at all sure she liked.

In a state of virtual trance, she walked with Nicolas up the steps to the front entrance where the door was opened to them by a man so old and bent that he looked like a caricature of the archetypical family retainer.

'Monsieur Nicolas!' he said, seizing the younger man's hands, the lined face lighting up with pleasure. 'We had begun to be afraid you were not coming, after all!'

'*Alors*, here I am, Jules,' Nicolas said, smiling down at the old man with genuine warmth. Then she saw his smile fade, his face close up as if a shutter had come down, as another man came in view.

'Uncle Bertrand,' he greeted him, quietly and a little stiffly.

'Nicolas. We thought you must have been delayed while driving back from Lyon.'

'I would have called if that were so, and I were unable to get here,' Nicolas said drily. 'That is why I have the cellphone in the car. Another small matter cropped up, but I did not think it would take too long to settle.'

The two men eyed one another. Given the disparity in years, the resemblance between them was remarkable, and yet Bertrand's mouth had something slack about it, his whole demeanour was less precise, lacking the purpose and dynamism of his nephew, so that they were more like opposite sides of a coin. Julia could see that there was no love lost between them, but it was the uncle who seemed ill at ease, rather than Nicolas, who strode across the hall as if he were quite at home.

'Is it him? Is he here?' a woman's voice called, and then the owner of the voice appeared in the open doorway of a room to the left. She was breathtaking, exquisite, a thick tumble of blonde hair framing a heart-shaped face, the slim, petite body of a young girl making her appear more like a woman in her twenties than one in her middle years.

'Tante Marguerite.' Nicolas accorded her the dutiful double kiss on alternative cheeks, and she stood back to look him over, something wistful about her expression.

'You look tired.'

'A little, maybe. I work hard,' he said pointedly.

'I know you do, Nic. *Je le sais.*' There was a hint of apology in her tone, and Julia felt the air swarming with nuances she could not understand. She forced a polite smile to her face as Nicolas introduced her to both of them as 'a friend from England', even though she felt more strongly than ever that she should not be here. There were untold tensions in this family which she would have had to be blind or totally insensitive not to divine, and they could prove a minefield for an innocent outsider. Nicolas should never have brought her here.

They moved into a long, elegant dining-room where aperitifs were served as they sat at the table, French fashion, to drink them, rather than standing around fielding glasses and canapés. The interior of the house, so far as Julia had seen it, was every bit as exquisite as the outside, the furniture mostly eighteenth-century, the superb wood panelling of the floor spread with fine Aubusson and oriental carpets. There was fine Limoges china and cut glass Bohemian goblets so delicate that Julia feared hers would snap in her hand, solid silver cutlery and candelabra.

The food was no less splendid. Questions rose in her throat as she ate her way through poached salmon and veal tournedos, a salad of young spinach and beetroot, a cornucopic cheese board and a rich *clafoutis* of fruit, egg custard and pastry. Her hosts seemed not in the least troubled by the arrival of an extra mouth to feed, and there was more than enough for everyone, including appropriately fine wines with each course, and an excellent old cognac afterwards.

A self-made man, Nicolas Lestrille, or so she had been led to understand. He had built up his company from nothing, devoted every minute of the last dozen years to its development and expansion. But from the look of his uncle's home, and the lifestyle here, there was serious money in the family. Hadn't any of it been put at Nicolas's disposal when he founded his business, and, if not, was that the cause for the coolness she sensed between him and his uncle?

Somehow, though, for all his less endearing traits, his arrogance and high-handed assumption of his own unerring rightness of judgement, she did not see Nicolas as a man who expected handouts and resented their absence. Once again she thought, as she had done before, Something does not fit. There was an enigma at the core of him, and she could not help sensing that the key to it was right here in this house.

But since it was unlikely that anyone would see fit to satisfy her curiosity on that score she did the only thing she could, and negotiated her way through the occasion with as much grace as she could muster, seeing that she was unexpected, uninvited, and hardly dressed for it. She answered

Bertrand and Marguerite's questions about various aspects of life in England, talked about her work and the exchange, and admired the château. It was a performance, she knew, and the hardest part of all was trying to behave naturally with Nicolas, as if they really were friends, not just two people inconveniently thrown together by an incident.

Darkness had fallen while they were eating, and, glancing covertly at the ormolu clock over the imposing marble fireplace, Julia was amazed to discover how late it was. She should really have phoned Anne-Sophie and told her she would not be home, especially as she did not have a key to get into the flat if the French girl had gone to bed.

She caught Nicolas looking at her with a faint question in his eyes, and realised that he had once again managed to tune in on her thoughts in that uncomfortably perceptive way that he had.

'We must be going,' he said, drinking the last of his coffee. 'Both Julia and I have to work tomorrow. And, since she has to escort a group of teenagers around Rouen, she probably needs the rest more than I do.'

'It was a pleasure to meet you, *mademoiselle*,' Nicolas's aunt said as she saw them to the door. She put her arms around him briefly, a tiny figure against him. 'Don't stay away so long this time, Nic.'

He detached himself gently, and Julia saw that while her devotion to him was almost frighteningly intense, his feelings for her were more ambivalent. It was all very strange, to say the least.

She was silent for a while as he steered the car back along the country lanes, dark and deserted now, and then finally, because it was foreign to her nature to restrain her thoughts for too long, she said, 'I had no idea that you came from that kind of background—Nicolas.' She hesitated slightly over the use of his first name, but, having called him by it all evening, she could not sensibly go back to 'Monsieur Lestrille.'

'Is it important?' he said distantly, his voice a little strained in the car's dim interior.

'No, but...I was surprised. And I felt a little out of place.'

'Because my uncle lives in a château?' His tone was acidic, and she began to wish she had not raised the subject.

'No, not entirely. That was the cause of the surprise, maybe. The discomfiture was more because I could sense that you and your uncle don't get on too well. That makes for a difficult situation for a stranger.'

He was quiet for a few moments, then she heard him sigh, and he pulled the car into the side of the road, switching off the engine as if his own thoughts were too heavy to combine with driving. Trees whispered eerily above them, but, apart from that, there was only the deep silence of the country all around, enveloping them like a cloak.

'You're right, of course,' he said after a short pause. 'There was a disagreement many years ago between my uncle and his brother, my father, who is now dead. It left a lot of bad feeling behind.' He paused again, and she saw that he had absolutely no intention of expanding on this any further. And why should he, after all? she thought with an intrinsic sense of fairness. He had said as much as he needed to say about it, considering the brevity of their acquaintance.

She was surprised, therefore, when he suddenly added, 'Would it make you feel better if I were to tell you that your presence made the evening considerably easier for me?'

Julia was momentarily astonished that he should be at all concerned about her feelings. A warm, glowing sensation began to spread through her body, a reaction she did not understand and certainly did not trust. She countered it as best she could by telling herself she was being juvenile and ridiculous.

'I was only there by accident, because you mistakenly got hold of the idea you had to take pity on me,' she said, a little sharply. 'If you had really wanted a partner for the evening, I'm sure you could easily have pulled one out of the queue!'

'*What queue*?' His voice was silky and mildly ominous in the darkness, and Julia realised, with a fearful sinking of the heart, that as she so often did, she had spoken without thinking first.

'Oh, come on, Nicolas—don't be coy!' she said lightly, trying to bluff her way out by turning the whole thing into a joke. 'You must know that you are considered to be one of Dieppe's most eligible men around town!'

'*Vraiment*? Is that a fact?' He was taunting her now, she could tell from his voice, although she could not see his face clearly. 'I wonder who you have been discussing me with?' He gave a low laugh. '*Alors*, if there really is a queue, then you would appear to have jumped it, wouldn't you, Julia?'

'I,' she said tartly, 'am not even in it, I do assure you! I've had enough of this nonsense, Nicolas. Would you please start the car and take me back to Dieppe?'

'It was you who started the so-called "nonsense", not I,' he reminded her drily. 'And since I am in the driving seat, I shall start the car when I am ready, and not a moment before. First of all——'

He broke off, and with a speed and directness she had not anticipated, Julia found she was in his arms, pinioned to the back of the seat, her head tipped back and his mouth on hers. She could not move. She could not even breathe, because Nicolas Lestrille was kissing her with a hard, ferocious intentness, bruising her lips and forcing them apart. It was no gentle first kiss, exploring or persuading. He took it for granted that she wanted it and welcomed it. Julia squirmed and threshed in her seat, but his upper body was hard against hers, and the pressure of his mouth was unrelenting. Briefly, she half wriggled free, but his hands gripped her shoulders firmly, and she could not escape. They were alone, miles from anywhere, and there was nothing to prevent him from doing anything to her. Anything he wanted . . .

The thought should have inspired her with fear, but suddenly she was filled with a racing excitement instead, and she was no longer fighting, but, amazingly, responding. The tension drained from her body, her mouth welcomed his invading tongue, her hands no longer pushed against him. Feeling the shift from resistance to surrender, he moved his weight from her, his hands sliding from her shoulders to her breasts. She could have moved away from him easily, now, but she no longer wanted to. A deep moan welled up in her throat as his fingers worked their way inside her shirt.

For perhaps half a minute he continued to caress her, expertly and pleasurably. Then he detached himself, of his own free choice, and slid back over his own side of the car. His breath was calm and even, his whole manner unruffled, as if he had never touched her.

'Now get back in the queue!' he said coldly, starting the engine and heading off once more towards Dieppe.

CHAPTER FOUR

THE door at street level was locked, not surprisingly, when Julia arrived back at Anne-Sophie's flat, and the French girl was none too pleased at having to come downstairs in her dressing gown to let her in.

'*Mon Dieu*, where have you been until this hour?' she said, her brow creased, her lips pursed in prim disapproval. Since it was not yet eleven o'clock, Julia had to suppress a surge of resentment at being spoken to as if she were a naughty schoolgirl who had broken her curfew.

'I'm sorry, I should have phoned you,' she apologised. 'There was a little problem with one of my students, which has all been sorted out.' She hesitated, knowing the other girl was unlikely to accept that sorting out a 'little problem' would have taken several hours. 'Then we...we had dinner,' she finished lamely, loath to go into details about her visit to the château.

Anne-Sophie's brows rose pointedly.

'You had dinner with Nicolas Lestrille?' she said, in faint surprise.

'Yes. Well, we were both hungry, and one has to eat.' Julia glanced at her watch. 'I'm really sorry to have disturbed you, but I must get to bed myself now. I have to take the students to Rouen tomorrow.'

The truth was that she did not want to answer any more questions, either about Kim's misadventure or her own evening with Nicolas. As it was, Anne-Sophie's penetrating, slightly accusing stare made Julia feel, quite irrationally, that what had happened in the darkened car was written all over her own guilty face.

She made herself scarce, relieved to close the bedroom door behind her, but even when lying in bed she seemed to see his face floating behind her closed eyelids, to hear his scathing voice saying, 'Now get back in the queue'. As if she had deliberately asked for his caresses and he had given her what he considered were her ration.

About the touch of his expert hands, and her own willing response to them, she dared not allow herself to think. It was too shaming. If she thought about it too deeply, she would have to admit to the brief pleasure she had taken in it, and that would not do. Turning over, Julia buried her hot face in the pillow, and tried to will her body to forget.

The following evening, the students, their French hosts, and their employers had planned a farewell party in the Café des Tribunaux. It was their last night in Dieppe, the culmination of a week of hard work, and a small celebration of the exchange's success was felt to be in order.

Julia knew she had to be there, that there was no way she could avoid it, but all day, as she shepherded her little troup around the historic city of Rouen, trying to direct the teenagers' attention to its immense Gothic cathedral and architectural glories, rather than its fascinating shops and cafés, a dread she could not suppress was building up inside her.

Nicolas was almost certain to be present. As one of the principal employers who had taken part in the scheme, and as an important figure in the community, his attendance would be required, and she could not see how, in the crowded bar, she could entirely avoid him. She wished fervently that she could find some way of sparing herself this embarrassment, but she knew it simply was not possible. For this one last time she would have to face him, remembering the events of the previous evening, knowing he would be doing the same ... that he would find a grim, perverse amusement in the memory.

'You are going to be wearing jeans?' Anne-Sophie said as Julia emerged from her bedroom ready for the short walk to the Tribunaux. There was a touch of disapproval in her voice, as if she did not think it suitable for a teacher to wear similar garb to her students.

'I feel comfortable in them, and it *is* a social occasion,' Julia said. They were well fitting black jeans, and with them she wore a black and white silk print shirt, and a short mohair jacket. Her hair was loose around her shoulders, and shone like silk. For all its casualness, she had taken a great deal of care over her appearance, and it was no use pretending that the likely presence of Nicolas Lestrille did not have a lot to do with it. Looking good was her first line of defence.

Anne-Sophie sniffed. She herself was in a neat two-piece she might have worn in the classroom, with a straight skirt and a Chanel-type edge to edge jacket. It was obvious from her manner that she considered Julia to be frivolous, and her attire totally out of place.

'If you are sure...' She shrugged coolly. 'We must go now, I suppose.'

The Tribunaux was full of people, as always. It was a café for all purposes—bourgeoise ladies drinking hot chocolate after their shopping forays, businessmen sipping pastis while they forged a deal—but, at night, the young claimed it as their own. The students had commandeered a corner, occupying several tables, and Julia could not but note, with approval, that they sat in a companionable group, mingling easily with the French counterparts they had first greeted so warily a few days ago.

She smiled and waved, and slid into a seat next to Olivier Gérard, guiltily thankful that Anne-Sophie had taken a place at a different table. There had most definitely been an air of constraint between them today. Silly, I wasn't *that* late getting in last night, Julia thought with annoyance.

'*Mes félicitations*, Mademoiselle Delaney, on a very successful exchange visit.' Olivier smiled.

'You're very kind,' Julia said graciously, her eyes darting covertly around the bar, and noting with relief that so far, at least, Nicolas was nowhere in sight.

'Not at all. It's a credit to you that there was only one small mishap, and you dealt with that with compassion and efficiency,' he said. His eyes rested with a twinkle on Kim, who, although white-faced and still a little fragile, had doggedly gone on the trip to Rouen with the others, and was here tonight, carefully sipping mineral water.

Julia stifled a groan.

'You heard? I suppose Nicolas told you,' she said ruefully.

'Nicolas Lestrille? *Mais non.*' Olivier shook his head emphatically. 'He would not discuss such a thing. But the young talk among themselves, and one overhears. The young lady has made considerable capital out of this story, with herself as the damsel in distress, and Nicolas as the rescuing knight in shining armour!'

Julia mentally cursed her own naïveté in expecting a seventeen-year-old girl to value discretion above drama.

'Oh, dear,' she said. 'Well, he was most helpful, I have to admit.' She stole a sidelong glance at her companion. 'Monsieur Gérard—did you know that Nicolas's uncle lives in a rather splendid château?'

'Of course. It's no secret. The name is actually *de* Lestrille. The prefix "de", as I am sure you will know, denotes a family of aristocratic origin, and this is a very old one,' he told her. 'You have seen the château?'

Having opened the subject, she could hardly deny it.

'I had dinner there last night,' she said shortly.

'*Mon Dieu*, you are honoured,' he said, giving her a strange look.

'Not really—it happened more or less by accident, after we had finished sorting out Kim,' she admitted. 'What's more, I felt a little uncomfortable. There's obviously no love lost between Nicolas and his uncle.'

'Ah.' Olivier tapped his glass with his fingers. 'It's an old story, and one worthy of de Maupassant himself,' he said. 'They were twin brothers, Bertrand de Lestrille and Nicolas's father, Eugene, but completely different in temperament. Eugene stayed at home and cared for the château and the land, whereas Bertrand was a complete wastrel, who took off and lived a dissolute life—gambling, women, spending money like water.'

'But I met Bertrand. I thought the château belonged to him,' Julia frowned. 'At any rate, he's still living there.'

'Under French law, it belonged to both of them,' Olivier said. 'But when Bertrand had spent up and had nowhere else to go, he came home, like the prodigal son. Eugene was engaged to a beautiful girl at that time—Marguerite. Bertrand somehow seduced her away from him and married her himself.'

Julia sucked in her breath.

'So what happened to Eugene?'

'It was very sad. Losing Marguerite seemed to take the heart out of him. He went away, leaving the château to his brother's mercies. Having got his hands on what remained of the inheritance,

Bertrand spent wildly and let everything go to ruin.'

Julia recalled the beautiful château in its immaculate grounds, the splendid food and wine.

'It's far from a ruin now,' she said.

'Thanks to Nicolas, only,' he replied. Seeing her raised, questioning brows, he went on, 'No one really knows what happened to Eugene after he left Normandy. Nicolas does not speak of it, except to say that his father is now dead, and one does not dare ask. Obviously, he married someone else. Nicolas came back here after finishing his studies, and proceeded to carve out an empire. It is his money which has restored the château and the family fortunes.'

'How very strange,' mused Julia. 'You would think it the very last thing he would do, considering the way his uncle had behaved, and the animosity between them.'

Olivier shook his head thoughtfully.

'Nicolas Lestrille is a very strange man,' he commented. 'Just, and honest, with a great deal of integrity, but very... driven. You would be ill-advised to try asking him about any of this.'

Julia shuddered.

'I wouldn't dream of it,' she said feelingly. 'Anyhow—he isn't here.'

'Oh, yes, he is,' Olivier corrected her. 'He has just arrived. See?'

It seemed to Julia that her heart leapt, then plummeted, all in the same fraction of a moment. She did not want to have to face him; she would have felt far more comfortable if he had not turned up. Yet a dizzy elation gripped her, almost as if she were glad to see him, and had been waiting for his arrival. Her eyes followed his progress across the room. He too was wearing jeans tonight, and a turtle-necked blue sweater, but his casual dress in no way lessened the sense of power that flowed from him. He moved in a force-field of his own, exuding a complex and dangerous authority that hovered always an inch behind his smile, and declared him to be constantly on battle alert, however relaxed he might appear. He was never off duty.

Now that he was here, she wanted to dispense quickly with that moment of confrontation, to get it over with and behind her. But he did not appear to have noticed her; either that or he was deliberately ignoring her presence. He stopped at virtually every table but hers, talking to the occupants, and, even when he was directly opposite her, his eyes never acknowledged her existence.

I was right the first time, thought Julia, he is rude and arrogant. She watched him from beneath lowered lashes, noting his sharp, crisp movements, the spare, effective gestures of those long-fingered hands, and, for a moment of total recall, she was once more back in the dark Normandy countryside, feeling those hands exploring her. A wave of some peculiar sickness washed over her, leaving her spent and weak, and she found herself gripping the arms of her chair tightly, for the sickness was not revulsion, it was desire. She hated him in that moment, and at the same time remembered his touch with intense pleasure.

This sensation was so deeply disquieting that she could not remain seated where she was, close to him but virtually excluded from the charmed circle of recognition he was casting around everyone else. Excusing herself, she eased past Olivier Gérard and went to sit by Kim, who was temporarily on her own. With her back thus turned to Nicolas, she endeavoured to ignore him as he was ignoring her.

'How are you feeling, Kim? Better now?'

'Loads better, thanks. I was a bit queasy on the coach today, but I'm glad I didn't miss Rouen.'

'And I should stick to soft drinks for the present,' said a voice behind Julia, which made her stiffen.

'Monsieur Lestrille, I promise you I never want to drink wine again!' Kim said earnestly, looking up with large, limpid eyes.

Julia refused to turn and follow the direction of the adoring gaze. But to her horror, Nicolas slipped into the seat next to her. She could feel the warmth of his flank next to hers, smell the astringently clean scent of him, and she wished he would go away—anywhere, so long as she need not be so blindingly aware of him.

'That's going a little too far. Never is a long time,' he said with tolerant humour.

'Hey—Kim!' Mark's voice called from across the smoky room, and, when the girl hesitated,

Nicolas said, 'Run along. I'll take care of teacher.'

Kim found this amusing, and giggled as she left them, but Julia did not.

'Teacher can take care of herself,' she said acerbically.

'Maybe,' he said, summoning a waiter with a flick of his hand and indicating that he wanted fresh drinks brought for them. 'When she wants to.'

'I don't know what that's supposed to mean,' she said. She still had not looked him in the eye.

'It means you can behave recklessly sometimes, Julia,' he said pleasantly, almost smugly.

And now, since she could not avoid it, she turned in her seat and glared icily at him.

'And you can behave abominably,' she retorted.

His gaze didn't flinch, but remained resting thoughtfully on her.

'You didn't find it abominable at the time, although it may suit you to pretend so, in retrospect,' he stated bluntly.

Julia was thankful for the smoke-filled atmosphere that concealed, to some extent, the pink tide creeping up her neck to her face.

'You're mistaken. I would advise you to stick to business, since that's all you really know,' she flashed.

'I wonder where you come by all these snippets of misinformation about me,' he said mildly. 'Anyhow, you should not underrate business as a good training ground for understanding human nature. I certainly know when I am in a position to clinch a deal.'

It took a moment for the meaning of this to sink in, and when it did, Julia, outraged and mortified, half rose in her seat and tried to push past him. But he turned towards her, resting one elbow on the table and the other arm along the top of the banquette, effectively blocking her escape.

'You have me cast as some kind of corporate robot, Julia,' he said in a firm, quiet voice. '*Alors*, so it is true I have had to work long and hard to get where I am. From necessity—no one gave me a lift up on to the ladder. But I am a man, as other men, in most respects. In summer I play tennis. I keep a boat, and enjoy messing about on it. In winter I ski. I enjoy the theatre, and I read a lot. Although I live in Dieppe for convenience, I love the countryside. You see? So don't try to put me in a box and stick a label on me.'

Julia stared at him, her eyes wide with surprise at this almost passionate self-exposition. She was remembering, reluctantly, her own instinctive appraisal, the suspicion that there was a piece missing from the picture, a dimension she had not discovered. Something that did not gel.

'I also have to say that, where women are concerned, my reactions are roughly similar to those of any other red-blooded male,' he added baldly.

Julia thought of the swift savagery of his kisses, the hard, restraining hands that had prevented her from struggling free.

'Oh, no, they are not!' she retorted fiercely. 'Where women are concerned, you are a barbarian!'

She had fully intended this to anger him, but, to her amazement, his response was a low, appreciative chuckle.

'You think so?' he said equably. 'Well, you were glad of it, were you not? In fact, I got the impression you would have liked me to be even more ... barbaric.'

Julia's face was thoroughly red now; her hands were quivering. He was reminding her, quite blatantly and without a vestige of good manners, let alone chivalry, that it was he, not she, who had decided enough was enough, and called an end to their embrace.

'I find you quite insufferable,' she said. 'It's fortunate that I shall be going back to England, so I shan't be obliged to meet you again. Now please let me pass.'

He stood up, and with a mocking, sweeping gesture of his hand indicated that she was free to go.

'By all means,' he said easily. 'You are not obliged to do anything you don't wish to. You never were. But you know that, don't you? And that is why you are so hot under the collar.'

His smile was infuriatingly knowing.

'I have learned a new expression tonight, from listening to the English students. *Chill out*. You know this one? Chill out, Julia. A few kisses in a car are nothing to get so excited about.'

She managed to avoid him for the rest of the evening. In fact, it wasn't difficult, for he made no further attempt to get close to her, or speak to her. He circulated among the gathering, having plenty to say to everyone else, and Julia could see that he was respected and admired by his fellow businessmen.

She could not escape the uncomfortable suspicion that he had only had one goal in mind in speaking to her at all. He had wanted to drive home the point that, according to him, it was she who had engineered their brief embrace in the car, she who had wanted his kiss and his touch, and had intentionally provoked him into giving her what she wanted.

But it had *not* been like that, Julia protested inwardly. Her remarks about his succession of eagerly waiting women had not been a hint that she wanted to be one of them. She had been surprised—no, shocked—when he had suddenly seized her in his arms. So his almost brutal kiss had aroused an answering need in her, and she was not proud of that, but she had not asked for it. At least, not consciously.

This was fast becoming ridiculous! She really could not start delving into the mysteries of what her subconscious mind wanted or did not want. That much introspection was unhealthy.

He had said it himself—a few kisses in a car were nothing to get excited about. She had to forget about it, to put it behind her as a brief incident which had simply happened. What troubled her was the awful feeling that with

Nicolas, nothing just 'happened'. He had not been carried away by a brief wave of desire. He had been making a point about his own will and his ability to dominate, to make the ground rules, at all times.

Ugh—I should *hate* to be one of his occasional women, Julia told herself firmly. No man was going to lay down the law to her, or to decide the parameters of a relationship without consulting her.

Across the room, she caught Anne-Sophie looking at her with a guarded suspicion. Surely she did not seriously think that Julia had joined the 'queue', that she had thrown herself at Nicolas Lestrille? She gave herself an impatient shake. It really did not matter what Anne-Sophie thought, and, as for Nicolas, he would soon be out of her life for good.

She left the Café des Tribunaux without speaking to him again, but as she went out through the door to the street she could not resist a swift backward glance.

He met it unsmilingly, and, even at this distance, the coldly mocking glint in his chameleon eyes sent a shiver down her back. A man to avoid, there was no doubt about it!

They were due to sail home on the afternoon ferry, which gave everyone time to browse around Dieppe's famous Saturday morning market, which took over the entire Grande Rue and much more of the town centre besides. Julia strolled

round with Chrissie, who was enthusiastically
filling bags with cheese and pâté to take home.

'Your arms will ache, carrying that lot,' she
grinned.

'I know, but I can't resist it, and I haven't
bought any cakes, yet!' Chrissie groaned.

As Julia had hoped, the young student teacher
had acquired much more confidence during the
week, and was now much more relaxed. The exchange had been the culmination of the school
year, and the long summer vacation was due to
start as soon as they arrived home, which had
put her in an even happier frame of mind, as she
babbled on about the holiday in Greece she had
planned to take with friends.

'What about you, Julia? Will you be going
away?' she asked.

To be honest, Julia had been so caught up in
organising the exchange that she had scarcely
given a thought to anything that lay beyond it.

'I haven't planned anything,' she admitted.

'I thought you were supposed to be going to
Florida with Adam?'

Julia grimaced. 'We did talk about it, earlier
in the year, but that's all over now, Chrissie,' she
said. And that was certainly true, she thought.
In fact, it was safe to say that she would not have
Adam back if he came crawling to her on his
hands and knees.

She was free, now, totally unfettered. If she
ever again, at any time in the future, became involved with a man, she would ensure that she
chose one who was strong enough in himself not

to feel threatened or diminished by a woman's success. One who ran his own life and played his own game.

Into these thoughts, Nicolas Lestrille came unbidden. 'Chill out, Julia', she heard him say amusedly, his intriguingly accented English lending the words a flavour all his own.

Not him, she thought, horrified that he had even come to mind in this connection. Strong was one thing, overbearing was another. But she could not help wondering wistfully how it might have been if he really had found her attractive, what it could have meant to look into those arresting, unusual eyes and see real desire in them. He was dangerous, no doubt—but exciting!

She shook off these thoughts determinedly.

'I might go to stay with my father in Bristol for a few days,' she said to Chrissie, but even as the words left her lips doubt set in.

'Come down if you like. You know you're always welcome,' Rosie always said, whenever Julia phoned to suggest it, but the very words she used made their meaning uncertain. Rosie was Liam Delaney's second wife, whom he had married, after a brief widowerhood, during Julia's first year at university. She was lissom and charming, he was madly in love with her, and already they had two young children. She was also only three years older than Julia.

Rosie was friendly enough, and Julia liked her, but when she visited, she always felt as if she were an interloper on their love. Liam was a clever man, a brilliant architect, an articulate, witty conversationalist and a bon viveur, but since marrying Rosie he seemed to have retreated into a world of bottle-feeds and nappy changes, and every minute that wasn't spent working was completely Rosie and baby orientated. A twenty-five-year-old daughter was an anachronism in that world, and that was exactly how Julia was somehow made to feel.

Nowadays, the elegant sitting-room in the lovely Georgian house in Clifton was usually littered with two-year-old Charmian's toys, and baby Joseph's plastic bath and accoutrements were laid out on the Persian rug in front of the fireplace. In her own childhood, all toys and such paraphernalia had had to be cleared up before her father came home from work, and he had insisted on finding his wife looking chic and un-ruffled, his daughter tidy, when he brought clients or colleagues home for drinks, as he frequently had. He did not, Julia had often heard him declare loftily, expect the house to look like a bear-garden.

Remembering Rosie, in her jogging-suit splashed with bath water, surrounded by pots of zinc ointment and talcum powder, Julia thought ruefully that perhaps men were always more tolerant the second time around. Her own offers to help with the children were always politely rejected, and, when she had suggested she baby-sat so that Liam and Rosie could go out together, Rosie had told her firmly that they did not do things that way.

'We believe in taking our children with us wherever we go,' she had said. 'Don't we, Liam?'

Julia had reflected that, however dearly one loved one's offspring, the romance of a relationship was not best kept alive by trying to eat *filet mignon* in a four-star restaurant accompanied by two tots. As it was, Charmian was usually trampolining on the sofa until ten-thirty at night, since Rosie did not believe in fixed bedtime routine, and there was never a moment Julia could snatch a quiet word with her father, alone or otherwise.

Julia shuddered. She did not think she could face Bristol, where the sense of being an intruder in this tight little family unit increased the longer she stayed. On the other hand... she glanced thoughtfully around the colourful market stalls. Today, the sun had come out with a vengeance, as if it had finally decided to declare that summer has arrived, and the air was warm. Apart from the trip to Rouen, she had not had time to see much of Normandy, and there was much she would have liked to see. The region appealed to her, and she found it attractive.

'Chrissie...' she said thoughtfully, 'I think I've changed my mind about visiting my father. What I really want to do is to stay here. Do you think you could cope with escorting the students home? All you have to do is see they don't create mayhem on the ferry, and hand them over to their parents who will be picking them up at Newhaven.'

Chrissie tore her attention briefly from a tempting display of pastries. A week ago, the mere idea would have given her severe palpitations, but now she barely hesitated.

'I reckon I could manage that,' she said. 'What will you do—stay on here in Dieppe?'

'Certainly not,' Julia said promptly, and without thinking, and when the younger girl shot her a questioning glance she very quickly invented the excuse that she did not get on all that well with Anne-Sophie, and did not want to be an unwelcome guest in her flat.

The reality was that, in her mind, Dieppe equalled Nicolas Lestrille, and the last thing she needed was to risk bumping into him. But he would be tied up with business, and he did not own the entire province! So long as she kept clear of Dieppe, she was unlikely to see him. With that infernal conceit of his, if she ran into him, he was sure to come to the conclusion that she had stayed on because she was secretly longing to pursue their acquaintance.

And that, of course, was far from being the case. Wasn't it?

CHAPTER FIVE

IT WAS with a feeling of mounting excitement that
Julia waved the ferry off as it pulled out of the
harbour, taking Chrissie and the students home.
Now she was really and truly free, without responsibilities, and could do exactly as she wished.

She had her driving licence and documents in
her handbag, as always, and so there was no
problem in hiring a small car. To begin with, she
took the coast road she had driven along with
Nicolas, only now she carried on further. The
sun grew warmer, the sea sparkled, and the
beaches below her were full of families enjoying
themselves.

With no preconceived idea of where she was
going, she drove into the small fishing town of
St Valery-en-Caux to take a break, and decided
to stay. Why, she wasn't sure—there were
probably resorts equally picturesque and more
commercial—but it seemed to her to encapsulate
all a Norman seaside town should be. It straddled
both sides of a river estuary, crossed by a bridge,
and in this calm inlet fishing boats and pleasure
craft bobbed amicably. There was a lively *centre-
ville*, with shops and cafés surrounded by brilliant flowerbeds, a square where no doubt
markets would be held, and a long sand and
shingle beach. This will do fine, she thought, and

sought out the nearest *agent immobilier* to see if she could find a property to rent.

There were several available, but the one that caught her imagination was right across the road from the yacht basin, a sturdy little grey granite ex-fisherman's cottage with tiny rooms, and a pocket-handkerchief garden full of rambler roses and hollyhocks at the rear. Here, she could wake up to a view of boats anchored mere yards away, and the sound of screaming seagulls. 'It's perfect,' said Julia, and paid two weeks' rent in advance.

Leaving the car parked outside, virtually at the water's edge, she walked into the town centre to buy a few essentials, and staggered back loaded down with baguettes, cheese, fruit, wine and pâté, wondering why shopping in France was so much more fun than the same chore at home! And there was a quiet contentment in sitting at her dining-table by the window that evening, eating her dinner while looking out at the marine comings and goings, then watching the sun sink slowly, and the lights come out across the river.

The awkward split with Adam was way behind her, and the situation with her father and his new family was an ongoing hurt she had learned to come to terms with. I can cope, she thought resolutely, snuggling down in the strange but comfortable bed, listening to the unfamiliar sounds of ropes and chains, creakings and lappings, in the darkness beyond her window. Being alone was not the end of the world, and at least, she had no one to please but herself.

She was up early in the morning, and after a quick cup of coffee, she dressed appropriately in jeans and a nautical blue and white striped top, her luxuriant black hair tied at the nape of her neck by a white ribbon, and strolled down to the quay for an entertaining half-hour eyeing up the freshly caught fish the boats had brought in, and buying some for her lunch.

It might have been as well to have asked the stall-holder to fillet it for her, she thought when she got home, laying it out doubtfully on the chopping board. Oh, well, she would just have to manage! She grasped a sharp knife, and, at that very moment, an unexpected sound made her pause with it held aloft.

Someone was knocking on the front door.

But no one knew she was here, apart from the estate agent who had rented her the house. Or had the neighbours come calling? Hardly likely. Forgetting she still had the knife in her hand, Julia called out, '*J'arrive!*' and went to open the door.

And there was Nicolas Lestrille, in navy trousers and a white sweatshirt, car keys dangling nonchalantly in one hand, calm, cool, and completely unfazed by the sight of her, while she— well, her mouth fell agape in sheer astonishment, her blue eyes were wide as dinner plates, and she was quite literally unable to speak a word.

'*Tiens!*' he said mildly. 'I come in peace. It is quite unnecessary to brandish that thing at me as if I were a Viking invader!'

Julia lowered her arm and the knife with it, and somehow forced her vocal cords back into belated action.

'But how…why…?' she stuttered, aware that, although they were working, they were not coming out with anything that sounded like sense.

'"How" is easy,' he said, a faint smile flickering across his face. 'My car is there—see?' And, indeed, Julia saw the white Mercedes convertible, the top down, parked alongside her hired car. '"Why"? Well, I happen to own this cottage, as I do several properties along the coast. Don't you think it would be polite to ask your landlord in and offer him a drink?'

Still bemused, Julia gestured for him to enter. Twenty miles or more she had driven from Dieppe to avoid chance contact with this man, and here he was, in this one place, this one particular cottage she had chosen to rent. Dazedly, she walked back into the kitchen, as if only returning to the occupation he had interrupted could restore her sense of balance, and he followed her in a leisurely manner.

'This has to be the craziest coincidence I have ever come across,' she said, almost accusingly.

He grinned.

'I know. It's just like *Casablanca*,' he said. Remembering the way he had spoken to her, only the night before, Julia tried to maintain a stiff demeanour, but she could not suppress a reluctant grimace.

'I've seen *Casablanca*, too, and you're not a bit like Humphrey Bogart,' she told him. 'What is it that you want, exactly, Nicolas?'

'How hospitable you are,' he said reprovingly. 'White wine will do, if you have any.'

She wanted to behave with cold formality. His manner towards her in the Café des Tribunaux had not been guaranteed to make them lifelong friends. But he seemed equally determined to forget it, and to act as if they were amicable acquaintances who had happened to run into one another by chance.

Reluctantly, she got out two glasses and poured wine from a bottle of Chablis she already had opened in the fridge.

'So you're the owner of this house?' she said, eyeing him cautiously as he stood, apparently quite at ease, sipping his wine and looking out into the tiny garden, in that fashion he had of appearing to be quite at home wherever he was. 'I had no idea of that, I assure you.'

'No, why should you?' he conceded. 'I use the place from time to time, but when I called in at the agent's to check if it was vacant he told me he had just let it to a Ms Julia Delaney. It seemed to me that there could not be too many of those at large. As you say, a strange coincidence. I imagined you had gone back to England with your students.'

'I decided to stay, on an impulse,' she said defensively, although what business it was of his if she wanted to see more of Normandy she was not quite sure. She should not have to excuse herself for being here. 'And now I expect you want me to move elsewhere, so you can have your cottage,' she went on, in a tone of strained annoyance. 'That's typical of you, Nicolas. I expect you think the whole world has to jump when you make a move. But I'm afraid I have paid two weeks' rent up front, and I happen to like it here!'

'There you go again, leaping to conclusions that have no foundation in fact,' he said, quite cheerfully. 'It must be that emotional Celt in you. No, I have no desire to turn you out into the street. My boat is moored in the yacht basin, and I can live quite comfortably on it for a short period.'

She stared at him.

'Your boat is here?' she echoed stupidly.

'That's right. I did tell you I had a boat. We Normans are a seafaring race, perhaps because we really do have Viking ancestry,' he said.

Taking in the compact strength of him, the proud set of his shoulders, and the all-conquering manner he wore around him, whatever he was doing, wherever he went, Julia could well believe it.

'Don't tell me you are actually taking a holiday!' she said with mild sarcasm. 'How will Lestrille S.A. manage to survive?'

He drained his glass and favoured her with a long, slow, humorous gaze.

'I am not glued to my desk in Dieppe, as you seem intent on presuming,' he said. 'I have a car phone, and I can be back at the office very quickly, if necessary. While I can't spare the time for a long absence, a day or two, or even a few hours, are vital for one's sanity, from time to time.'

His eyes moved from her to the fish lying on the worktop where she had left it. 'Are you planning on filleting that? If so, you have the wrong knife. Excuse me.'

He made to open a drawer at the side of her, and Julia virtually jumped out of his way. She did not want him accidentally to touch her—he made her distinctly nervous—nor did she want to give him any excuse for believing that she *did* want his touch. But he gave no sign of having observed her agitation. Taking a long, thin, murderous-looking knife, he parted the fish cleanly from its backbone in one swift, neat operation.

'*Voilà*,' he said with satisfaction. 'Those who fish have to know also how to prepare their catch. What a shame there is only enough for one, so you can't ask me to stay for lunch.'

'Whatever makes you think I would have done so?' she retorted tartly.

'Ouch! You are determined to find me unlikeable, aren't you?' he said, smiling with infuriating unconcern. 'Or are you this prickly with everything male?'

Everything male does not lunge at me in parked cars, and then make out I gave it the come-on, Julia was tempted to retort. But she was deeply reluctant to dredge all that up to the surface again. Her own part in the incident had not been as entirely involuntary as she would have liked to pretend, and she was aware that if she opened up the argument again she would be defending a weak position.

'I'm only prickly with people with whom I have nothing in common,' she said coolly.

'You can't say that, Julia, because you do not know me,' he said, with unexpected gravity. 'You know only some cardboard cut-out you have invented, which you persist in thinking is me. However—*ça m'est égal*. It's all the same to me.' He shrugged. 'Enjoy your lunch, and your stay in my cottage. *Au revoir*.'

In spite of a strong resistance, she could not fight the compulsion which made her go through to the living-room and watch his departure. Just as he had said, a spanking white cabin cruiser was moored in the *port de plaisance* directly opposite the cottage, and she followed him with her eyes as he swung easily on deck, and disappeared below.

Her appetite for the freshly caught fish was quite gone, and she had to force herself to cook and eat it. Sitting at her table, although she could not see him, she could see his wretched boat, and knew that he was there, and as she forced herself to swallow each mouthful of food, her innocent pleasure with the house, with St Valery itself, and all the things she had found so delightful only yesterday, drained away from her.

Why, why, why did he have to be here? Her peace was totally destroyed by her knowledge of his presence, and the unavoidable sensation that he knew she was disturbed by it, and found the whole situation vaguely amusing.

She toyed fleetingly with the idea of packing up and moving on elsewhere, but a fierce inner resolve refused to let her throw in the towel that easily. What—let him think she found him so disconcerting that she had to run away from him? Not a chance! Julia thought defiantly, clattering the dishes into the sink. She would simply ignore him and go about her holiday as if he were not there. Pretty soon, he would be on his way, she felt reasonably sure. Business would draw him back inexorably to Dieppe, whatever he said, and then she could enjoy the rest of her stay, just as she had planned.

Even though she would still be living in his house, and troubled by the possibility that he could turn up here at any time? But why should he? she asked herself. His boat was here, and mere curiosity had impelled him to find out if the same Julia Delaney he had met in Dieppe were renting his cottage. That was all. *'Ça m'est égal,'* as he had said. It was all the same to him.

And to me, too, she thought rebelliously. She was not going to skulk in here like a prisoner because he was around. Grabbing a sweater, she slung it casually round her shoulders. She was going to go out.

He was on the quayside. There was no way of avoiding him, or of pretending she had not seen him, because his appearance stopped Julia dead in her tracks. He had changed into a pair of old, paint-smeared jeans, and a disreputable sweater that looked as if it had seen better days, but not recently! His face was dirt-streaked, and there was a strong whiff of tar and paint clinging to him. Oddly enough, he exuded an aura of boyish insouciance, as if all the burdens and worries of executive responsibility had temporarily slipped from his shoulders.

He grinned happily at her.

'You must excuse the lack of sartorial elegance,' he said. 'I did come down to do some maintenance work on the boat, after all.'

'Yourself?' said Julia, astonished.

'Well of course *myself*,' he echoed with a touch of exasperation.

'I thought you paid other people to do all your menial jobs,' she said.

'At the office, yes—that's called delegation. My time is valuable, and has to be used where it's most essential.' He picked up the can of paint and replaced the lid. 'The whole point of having a boat is doing these things oneself, with one's own hands. It's therapeutic.'

'Thank you, Monsieur Bricolage, for those words of wisdom,' Julia said with a mock bow. She did understand, of course. It was the same need to switch off the brain and relax through physical exertion that sent her trudging the South Downs Way at weekends. Only her stubborn inability to see Nicolas Lestrille as human, sharing human needs and weaknesses like the rest of mankind, had clouded her appreciation of what he was trying to do.

'You are welcome,' he said unworriedly. 'Come aboard and have a look. I was just about to make some coffee.'

She hesitated. Only minutes ago she had declared her intention of ignoring him, behaving as if he were not there. The plain fact was that he was a difficult man to ignore. An even plainer truth was that she was nervous of coming in too close an orbit of him. Physically and mentally, he had a disquieting effect on her, and it was wisest not to expose herself to it unnecessarily.

'Unless you get seasick very easily, you are in no danger,' he told her. 'She's not going anywhere until her paint's dry, so I shan't kidnap you and put out to sea, if that's what you're afraid of.'

Since she could not allow him to get hold of the idea that she was in *any* way afraid of him, that decided her, and with a shrug of her shoulders she followed him along the wooden gang-plank. Negotiating the ladder to the deck, he held out a hand to help her up, and it was difficult to find a way to refuse it. His fingers were hard and firm, and the shock she felt each time he touched her ran along her nerves, familiar, remembered, and yet every time fresh and electrifying. She fought to control the tremor of her hand, without too hurriedly disengaging it from his. It was far from easy.

Below deck, it was surprisingly spacious—a neat, well equipped galley opening out into a comfortably upholstered saloon, but to Julia it still felt too confined an area to be sequestered in with Nicolas Lestrille.

'It's home from home,' she said, trying to make casual conversation. 'I mean, you could live quite comfortably on board.'

'Oh, yes.' He busied himself with the coffee, all his movements swift, spare and efficient. 'There's a decent master bedroom and two smaller bunkrooms, a shower and the usual offices. But it's too fine a day to be below. Now you've seen it, let's go back up on deck.'

Yes, let's, thought Julia, with intense relief. On deck there was sky and space all around, and she could escape a little from this pressing awareness of him. They sat on cushioned folding arm-chairs, drinking coffee, with the soft lap of water and the muted hammerings and tappings of other sailors working on their boats all around them. The sun was warm on Julia's face, Nicolas stretched out his legs and let his free hand trail over the arm of his chair, and something very odd happened. For a brief space of time, she found herself to be totally and completely re-laxed, with nowhere else she wanted to be, nothing at all she wanted to do but to sit here in companionable silence with this man at her side.

'I ask myself,' he said quietly, all at once, 'why this attractive, vivacious and personable young woman is here on holiday, all alone. To me, it seems very odd.'

Julia sat up straight, her peaceful mood of moments ago completely shattered, and all her nerves ajangle once more.

'And I ask myself what on earth it has to do with you?' she snapped.

He ignored her outburst, shifting his relaxed attitude only slightly in a half-turn towards her.

'Perhaps she has been disappointed in love, and has come here to lick her wounds?' he mused. 'But then, she seems so full of strange moods and emotions...like a cat whose fur has been ruffled the wrong way...I wonder if perhaps there is something her life lacks, which would make her at one with herself.'

Julia set her cup down on the deck with a ringing firmness, and stood up.

'There is nothing lacking in my life, you can take that as definite,' she stated in clear, haughty terms. 'I know exactly what you are hinting at, and, let me tell you, if there *were* anything I needed, you would be the last man I should come to in search of it. Is that perfectly clear?'

He stood up, too, and looked down at her with a challenging light in his eyes which, at that moment, shone deepest amber.

'*D'accord,*' he said lazily. 'In that case, since we have no wicked intentions in regard to one another, there is no reason why we should not go out for a drive together tomorrow. Is there?'

She managed to tell him, firmly and categorically, that she did not want to go out anywhere with him, thank you very much. She even managed to climb back down the ladder without his help, since he did not offer any, and without falling flat on her back, or taking a dive into the harbour.

What she did not succeed in doing was shutting him out from her thoughts. Even when, mercifully, it was dark enough to close the curtains, and she did not have to see his boat every time she looked out of her window, she could not get rid of the nagging awareness that he was *still there*. She tried to read a book, but his annoyingly, intriguingly handsome face kept intruding between the printed page and her own concentration. And when she finally retired to bed, she still felt enmeshed in a reluctant intimacy with him, as if an invisible silken thread linked her to him, a short space away across the quay.

How dared he assume—how could he have the effrontery to believe she would want to go out anywhere with him? Did he think that she had been sent by a benevolent providence to amuse him and enliven his visit here, and that he had only to suggest, and she would immediately fall in with his plans? To hell with that, Julia thought angrily.

The blissful sleep of the previous night was not easy to achieve; consequently she awoke later than she had intended. Padding down to the kitchen, barefoot and in her pyjamas, to make coffee, she saw the garden already brilliant with sunshine—and incredibly, sitting comfortably on a wooden chair she was sure had not been there yesterday, was Nicolas Lestrille.

Julia forgot that she was in her nightclothes, her hair unbrushed and dishevelled. Flinging open the back door, she said in a low, furious voice, 'What on earth do you think you are doing here?'

'Good morning to you, too,' he said with a wry smile. 'I thought you were never going to wake up. I've already done two hours' painting on the boat, and coffee would be very welcome, thank you.'

'You have no right to be here when I have not invited you,' she shot at him. 'It's bad enough you being in St Valery at all, with your boat practically moored on the doorstep, without my having to find you camped in the garden. I shall complain to the agent!'

He inclined his head slightly.

'You could try, but I am the proprietor, remember, so I don't think you would get very far. I have already told him we are old friends.'

'Then I shall move somewhere else. There must be houses along this coast that you don't own.'

'Run away? Don't tell me I have overestimated you, Julia.' He stood up. 'It looks as though I shall have to make the coffee myself, doesn't it?'

To begin with, she stood her ground as he advanced towards her. But he was fully dressed and she wasn't, and that made her vulnerability all the greater, and as the distance between them diminished, until only inches separated them, she realised that if she did not step aside he was going to move her—physically—himself. The brush of his fingertips, their hard grip through the thin stuff of her pyjama jacket, even in imagination, was more than she could equably endure. She backed inside, just in time, and with an air of satisfaction he set about brewing coffee.

'Take that with you and drink it while you get dressed,' he said. 'I'll wait. We can have breakfast somewhere *en route*.'

'Nicolas, I told you yesterday I did not intend going out with you,' she said.

'I know. But that was yesterday. This is today. And it's the best chance you have of getting me out of the house,' he said easily.

Julia stared at him for a long moment, defiance and resignation fighting an unequal battle. That he was quite adamant she did not doubt. He wasn't going to leave voluntarily, and she could not force him to do so. Turning to go upstairs, she suddenly looked back at him over her shoulder, her dark hair falling forward and partly veiling her puzzled face.

'Why?' was all she said, but he appeared to understand the question perfectly.

'Why? Let's say because when I make up my mind to do something I usually carry my intentions through. I don't like to be thwarted,' he said. Then he shrugged. 'Or why not just say it's a lovely day, and it would be more interesting to share it? Take your pick.'

CHAPTER SIX

THE first alternative, every time, Julia thought grimly as she ran up the stairs. She could see no reason why Nicolas should want to share his day with her; he purely and simply was accustomed to having his own way at all times, and even on so trivial a matter as this he was temperamentally unable to take no for an answer.

But why had he asked her in the first place?

Julia could not answer that question, and gave up the attempt. Having no idea where they were going, either, she was not sure how to dress. In the end, she settled for a floaty summer skirt and matching sleeveless top, in mingled shades of blue and pink, and went back downstairs to rejoin him.

She found him installing yet another wooden chair and a small table in the garden.

'These live in the shed at the bottom of the garden when not in use,' he said. 'You might want to sit outside, since the weather is fine. Feel free to do a spot of weeding and so forth, if the mood takes you. I never have the time.'

She did not know whether to be touched by his consideration, or annoyed by his proprietorial attitude.

'You'll regret it, if I do. I should probably dig up all the wrong things,' she said darkly. 'Besides, it's not my idea of a holiday activity.'

'What is, I wonder?' he said, as they went out to where the Mercedes was parked. Julia saw fit to ignore this remark. Instead, she glanced at the boat, sparkling and gleaming with new paint, and now he had picked out the name in fresh black and gold lettering, she read what she had missed yesterday: '*La Liberté*'.

'Freedom,' she said aloud. 'Is that what the boat represents to you?'

He shrugged. 'Perhaps. It's an illusion, of course. There isn't any. We are hedged about with constraints and responsibilities from the moment of our birth. One can only briefly pretend to escape.'

He opened the car door for her, and, sliding into her seat, Julia looked up unexpectedly and met his eyes. They were agate, and there was a bitter sadness in them she knew he had not intended her to see, for he suddenly forced a smile. 'Let's pretend.'

At the pretty village of Veules les Roses, they stopped for hot chocolate and croissants at a café, and then turned inland.

'I did think about visiting Monet's house at Giverney,' Nicolas said. 'It's beautiful, but at this time of the year sure to be crowded, and you would not be able to see the famous lily pond for the visitors.'

'Then where are we going, or is one not allowed to ask?' Julia demanded.

'One must wait and see,' he said, casting her an oblique smile. 'Don't you like mysteries, Julia?'

'The whole of life is a mystery to me sometimes,' she said ruefully, and he grinned sympathetically.

'You have a point. But this one I am sure you will enjoy.'

And she did, when they turned in at a château familiar to her from photographs, but which she had never seen in reality—the château of Miromesnil.

'It's the birthplace of the writer, Guy de Maupassant,' she said, surprised.

'I know. Your A level students have him on their literature curriculum,' he replied, and she shot him an even more astonished glance.

'How did you know that?'

'*You* told me. The very first time we met, when you took my office by storm. You said you would be marking essays all night.'

She inhaled deeply.

'Is your memory always this reliable?'

'Always,' he said, with a cheerful lack of modesty. 'You don't get anywhere by being slipshod.'

With this man, Julia thought, as they strolled in the château grounds, it was unwise to make a casual comment and assume it would be forgotten with equal casualness. In fact, it was unwise to take anything for granted. He had a mind as sharp, as complex and as thorough as a computer.

'De Maupassant's family, as I expect you know, fell on hard times and came down in the world,' he said. 'He had to break off his education and take a poorly paid job as a minor civil servant. It must have been hard, when he was born in a place like this.'

'I get the feeling you're identifying with him,' she observed, and his expression sharpened as he looked back at her.

'How do you mean? I wasn't born in a château,' he said. 'Who have you been talking to about me?'

'Oh...no one in particular...it's just odd things people happened to mention in Dieppe,' she faltered evasively, wishing, as ever, that she had kept her mouth shut. The morning had passed reasonably pleasantly, and she found she did not want to start arguing with him again.

Unexpectedly, though, his brief annoyance ebbed away, and he sighed resignedly.

'I have nothing to hide, truly, but sometimes I wish people would be less interested in my family's past,' he said. 'I am what I am—now.'

'It's not that simple, Nicolas,' she contradicted him. 'We are all partly shaped by the past—by things over which we have had no control.'

He was silent as they walked back to the car and got in, and only as he started the engine, he said, 'So—what *were* you told?'

'About how your uncle Bertrand, who was the black sheep of the family, spent all his money then came back and cheated your father out of his inheritance, and his fiancée.' She paused. 'And how you've used your money to restore the château, and to improve your uncle's lifestyle.'

'What was I supposed to do—let that wonderful old building, which has been in the family for so long, fall into ruins?' he challenged. 'Or, having restored the fabric, leave my relatives camping out in it like squatters? Besides, I do feel genuinely sorry for my aunt Marguerite. I'm sure she realised long ago that she married the wrong brother. There is my cousin Laurence to consider, too.'

'Laurence? I didn't meet her, did I, when . . . when you took me to dinner with your aunt and uncle?'

'No, she was away at college. She's their only daughter, a sweet kid, only nineteen. None of what happened has anything to do with her, so why should she suffer?' He shrugged. 'Uncle Bertrand has to live with the knowledge of what he did. In a sense, there's a more subtle revenge in heaping coals of fire on his head than in leaving him out in the cold.'

His smile was very slightly malicious, and Julia shivered in spite of the day's warmth.

'I wouldn't like to make an enemy of you, Nicolas,' she said.

'Then don't,' he said tersely. 'There is, anyhow, no reason why you should. Let's go and have lunch. I have a fancy for a good plate of *fruits de mer*. Will you share it with me?'

She did, in a restaurant overlooking the sea and the folds of tumbling white cliffs stretching forever along the coast; they cracked, split and crunched their way through a *plâteau* for two, of lobster, oysters, mussels, crab, and every kind of shelled and crustacean delicacy imaginable, all served up with a tray of implements for removing them from their shells, worthy of a surgeon's kit, and a bottle of dry Muscadet.

They drove back to St Valery via an inland route, stopping often to admire the lush, peaceful countryside, inhabited only, or so it seemed, by creamy cows munching the grass. Once they stopped by a lovely old manor house, creeping ivy all but smothering its grey walls, with a conical turret at one corner, and a stream running by.

'What a beautiful house, and in such a lovely spot,' she said enviously. 'I should love to live here!'

'I'll bet there are trout in that stream,' Nicolas mused. 'I'd like to tickle a couple, but they would probably see me and set the dogs on me.'

Julia was horrified.

'You aren't serious—you wouldn't!' she gasped. 'Anyhow, you can buy trout from the fishmonger in St Valery.'

'That's not the point, Julia,' he grinned. 'Ah—you don't have a hunter's instincts. Don't worry, I shan't poach. Not while I have teacher with me!'

She saw he was teasing, but the mockery was good-natured, and it did not make her angry.

'I should hope not! I'd give you a hundred lines to do,' she responded jokingly, and he slammed the fence with one hand.

'*Bon sang*!' he exclaimed. 'Is that all? I was hoping for a detention!'

She turned and leaned back against the fence, and he rested both hands on it, one either side of her. But his body did not touch hers, and now, perversely, she found herself hankering for its lean hardness against her. Waiting once again for him to kiss her, as he had before, as if she had been in suspense ever since. Unconsciously, her head had tipped back slightly, her eyes half closed, imagining, wordlessly inviting the touch of his hands she remembered so clearly.

He did not kiss her. She felt him move away, and perhaps he reckoned it was not worth the trouble, in view of the way she had over-reacted before. Or perhaps she was mistaken, and he did not want to kiss her at all, she thought soberly; perhaps his suggestive comment had been just one of those silly things a man said to a woman, meaninglessly.

The idea of Nicolas saying *anything* meaningless did not ring true, but there was no way she could know why he had changed his mind.

'We should be going,' he said practically, breaking the spell.

Julia cast a last, regretful glance at the house, a sharp stab of imagination peopling it with *her* friends dining al fresco by the stream, and in the evening, when they had left, a man walking with her across the grass, his head bent to hers . . . *her* lover?

This was silly—all because of a place she had not seen before and probably never would again,

she reproved herself as she slid back into the
Mercedes.

Afternoon shades were beginning to lengthen
across the harbour as they drove back into St
Valery.

'I have a bit more work to do on *La Liberté*'s
engine tonight,' Nicolas said. 'By tomorrow, the
paint will be dry, and I'm going to take her out.
Want to come?'

'Oh, but——' said Julia, and stopped, re-
alising, astounded, that she *did* want to. Very
much. 'All right. Thank you, I'd like that,' she
said. 'But I warn you, I don't know anything
about boats.'

'You don't need to. I know all that's necessary,'
he said, and there was nothing boastful nor even
complacent about his words or his manner. It was
a simple statement of fact. 'All the same, wear
a swimsuit. We shall be getting wet at some point
of the procedure.'

What a difference a mere twenty-four hours
could make, Julia thought next morning, as she
pulled on jeans and a sweatshirt over her bikini.
The day she had been so reluctant, initially, to
spend with Nicolas, she now looked back on with
a tingle of excitement...excitement that coloured
her anticipation of the day to come.

Away from the heavy responsibilities of the
office, he seemed a different man. The contours
she had been too ready to condemn as hard, grey
and inflexible had softened to reveal shades and
nuances of character she had not suspected. Or
perhaps not allowed herself to suspect?

Was this dangerous? she asked herself as she brushed her hair and wound it into a long plait to keep it moderately tidy. It was only a day out! Could she be risking the hazard of finding Nicolas Lestrille too fascinating... wanting to know more about this new, inner man she had glimpsed? She already knew beyond question that he attracted her physically, that she was both afraid of and eager for his touch.

She had to control that desire, for its only end was to be one of Nicolas's short-lived and emotionless affairs, and Julia was definitely not inclined to be so used.

Outside, the water sparkled in the sunshine, and the day waited. Julia cast off this heavy introspection and decided to take the day as it came. She was not a child, and she could take care of herself.

'Welcome aboard,' he said, giving her a hand up on deck, and looking her over with a gleam of approval in his eyes. 'I see you have succeeded in looking very chic, and being suitably clad at the same time. Just remember, though, that on this craft the captain's word is law.'

Julia withdrew her hand, trying to ignore the tingling of her fingers.

'What's new?' she said. 'I thought your word was law wherever you happened to be, Nicolas?'

'You are making me out to be a rigid authoritarian, and that's not entirely fair,' he protested, smiling faintly. 'Yes, I like my own way, and I usually think I am right, but I'm not totally insensitive to the views of others. But on a boat, too much anarchy could be dangerous.'

'I promise not to mutiny,' she said solemnly, and he grinned, picking up the hint of mischief in her blue eyes. 'As I told you, nautically speaking, I am a complete ignoramus.'

'Nautically speaking, this boat is a piece of cake,' he told her. 'I'll let you have a go at steering her once we're clear of the harbour.'

The calm waters of the yacht basin were, of course, illusory, and out at sea there was a moderate swell. Julia knew a moment's queasiness, and hoped fervently that she was not going to prove to be a bad sailor. She did not think she could bear Nicolas's amused contempt of such weakness. Somehow, it had become fiercely important that he did not dismiss her as a silly woman who felt ill and had to lie down at the first heave of the deck. She fixed her gaze firmly on the horizon, took a deep breath of fresh, salty air, and told herself the nausea would pass.

Miraculously, it did, and within half an hour she had adapted to the swaying motion of *La Liberté*. As Nicolas suggested, she took a hand at steering for a while, although the most difficult aspect of that was the feel of him standing behind her, very close, guiding her hands. The warmth of his body and his breath, the firm strength of his hand on her arm were almost more than she could endure and remain calm.

What was happening to her? she wondered faintly, relinquishing control to him as he guided them into the port at Fecamp. He had not appeared at all troubled by his proximity to her, so why did she have to suffer this burning, melting sensation inside, when he so much as touched her? Why did she feel so agitated that she longed for him to move away, and then, the minute he did, crave desperately for the contact to be resumed? It was all rapidly ceasing to make much sense.

'I thought we could raid the shops for a picnic lunch,' he said, as they strolled ashore. 'Then, if you don't mind a walk and a bit of a climb, there is a beach which is usually quiet, where we can eat and have a swim.'

The 'bit of a climb' he had so casually referred to was a steep scramble up rocky cliffs via a path that at best was tortuous, and at worst non-existent. Julia was glad Nicolas had charge of the bag full of food and drink and towels, because she needed both hands and both feet to remain upright, and even then she dared not look back.

Reaching the top, he turned and saw her clinging to a rock, momentarily unable to move. He smiled and held out his hand for her to grasp, and this time, she seized it gratefully, glad of the easy strength with which he hauled her up beside him.

'You certainly know how to give a girl a hair-raising experience!' she panted, only now risking a glance back whence she had come. 'What's next—abseiling for beginners?'

'It's easier going down,' he laughed. 'And worth it, I promise you.'

He was right. The beach, when they had scrambled down to it, was entirely enclosed by protective cliffs, and, not surprisingly, the clean crescent of golden sand was quite deserted. Far out at sea, the blue-green rollers creamed and tossed, but here, they trickled, tame and friendly, on to the shore of this small haven.

'Swim first?' he suggested, standing the bottle of wine he had bought in a shady rock pool to keep it cool. 'It will give us an appetite.'

Taking off her jeans and sweatshirt, she tried not to watch him divesting his, but the temptation was too great. His body was firm and classically proportioned, the length and size of his calf muscles just as they should be, a line of dark blond hair running up the centre line of his torso. He glanced up and caught her watching him, and a slow, sensuous smile spread across his face as his eyes travelled over her, in their turn, taking in the slim length of her legs, the curves of her breasts and the contrasting flatness of her stomach.

Icy shivers rippled through her as she endured this scrutiny, and all at once she could take it no longer. Turning, she ran down to the sea's edge, splashing through the shallows and plunging into the green depths beyond.

It was cold, and she came up choking and gasping from the chill, but once accustomed to it she surrendered quickly to the invigorating waves once more. She heard him coming up strongly beside her, saw his arm cleave the water, and then he was close, diving under and breaking the surface again, his hair curling damply round the nape of his neck, water clinging to his face and shoulders.

He struck out, to where the fiercer waves churned and boiled, and she followed him, not to be outdone, knowing a moment's fear in the strong current. Then the fear was gone as she found him at her side, and the strangest feeling came over her that, with him, she could risk danger, stretch herself to limits she had never previously known, and come through intact.

Maybe that was why, when he shouted, 'Far enough—don't go out any deeper!' she obeyed without hesitation, instinctively trusting his judgement where these waters he must know well were concerned.

She was breathless as they made the beach, but her eyes were bright with exhilaration, and there was respect in his.

'It was rough out there,' he conceded. 'You'll try anything, won't you? You have real spirit, Julia, I'll say that for you.'

Even as she warmed to the compliment, a questioning voice inside her was asking, Is it a test? Does he subject all his women to this kind of personal challenge? And if they fail—what then? They don't see him any more, presumably. Towelling herself dry, she thought rebelliously, I'm not going to be measured against some sort of scale, and graded accordingly.

She turned towards him in a brief flare of resentment, but she could not maintain it. It faded as she watched him expertly de-corking the wine bottle, then venting an amused expletive as the plastic cups, caught by a sudden breeze, bowled across the sand. She laughed, retrieving them, holding them steady as he poured, and then they both rummaged in the bag for the bread and the delicacies they had bought from the *charcuterie*— thinly sliced spicy sausage, cartons of taboulleh and mushrooms *à la grecque*, dressed crab piled artistically back into its shells.

The sun had grown stronger, and, replete with food and healthy exertion, Julia lay back on the sand, contemplating another swim in a while, when she had digested her lunch. Her eyes were half closed as she drifted into that somnolent state between waking and sleeping, the distant roar of the sea in her ears.

And then she was conscious of a shadow falling across her, and, opening her eyes, she saw Nicolas leaning over her, propped on one elbow.

'You are very lovely, Julia,' he said, his voice quiet, but throbbing with intensity.

She did not move, but gazed up at him, silent, expectant, and for a moment it was enough to be caressed and explored by his eyes as they moved slowly over her. Then it was no longer enough. She needed his kiss, he bent over her, and her waiting lips were already parting slightly, but his did not touch her there. Instead, his head inclined lower, and, startled, she felt his mouth on the bare skin of her navel.

She moaned, stirred slightly, and his lips continued their progress, imprinting themselves on her ribcage, and moving up, slowly; he rolled over, taking her with him until she lay on her side facing him, and now his mouth had found her breast, his hand lightly easing the strap down over her shoulder.

It must have been clear to him from the eager arching of her body, the dreamy sensuality awakening in her blue eyes, that she was of no mind to struggle or protest against the intimacy of this caress. Every nerve, every particle of her skin was living to the full the pleasure of his touch, revelling in sensations fiercer, sweeter than she had ever known before.

Then, suddenly, he raised his head, shaking it slightly, and released her, abruptly shifting to a seated position. Again, as yesterday, by the manor house, it seemed to Julia that an enchantment had snapped all at once, that he had briefly allowed himself to drift under its spell, and then, in the blink of an eye, remembered himself and climbed back into an emotional suit of armour.

Through the haze of personal rejection and frustrated desire, Julia was aware of an even stronger emotion emanating from him. She sensed him being torn apart by a superhuman struggle, knew that he had wanted her in that moment as much as she had wanted him, and had deliberately, and with an immense effort, denied himself.

'Nicolas? What...what's wrong?' she asked quietly.

He stood up, a sudden charge of energy impelling him.

'Nothing. Nothing at all,' he said harshly. 'I'm going for another swim. Are you coming?'

CHAPTER SEVEN

THERE was no mention, during their journey back to St Valery, of those sexually charged moments on the beach when he had seemed intent on making love to her, and then, for reasons known only to himself, had consciously decided against it.

Julia thought it advisable to say nothing. For one thing, how could you ask a man, 'Why did you suddenly go cold on me?' Even in the twentieth century, the initiative in making love, at least for the first time, still seemed to rest with the man.

Nicolas, from the very beginning, had struck her as the most virile, most masculine specimen of manhood she had ever come across, and she knew that back there on the beach he had actively desired her. Something had prevented him from going ahead, in spite of the powerful surge of need flowing through his veins.

Would she have let him? Julia wondered, glancing obliquely at him as he steered *La Liberté* back into harbour. Could she have stopped him, she asked herself wryly, and, more to the point, would she have had the will to stop him, or even try, when her own body had been screaming for more?

117

They parted on terms of intentionally cool formality, as if an invisible line were drawn on the floor between them, and they knew it would be fatal to cross it, by even an inch, and they made no arrangements to meet again.

But in the morning, she had no sooner opened her curtains than he was knocking at her door.

'Let's go to Rouen,' he said briefly, his tone indicating that he had no doubt she would accept.

She did. She could have sat on her high horse and given him a dignified refusal, but by now Julia was past denying that she was strangely hooked on Nicolas Lestrille. Beyond the addictive charm of his physical charisma, which was considerable, she yearned to understand what drove and motivated him, and made him the hard-shelled, inwardly sensitive character she suspected he was.

So she wandered the old streets of Rouen with him, exploring the ancient Rue du Gros Horloge, spanned by its Renaissance clock house, stood in the Vieux Marché where Joan of Arc had met her gruesome death, and gazed admiringly at the splendidly carved façade of the great cathedral.

'Of course, you have been here before, with your students,' he said.

'Yes, but I was too busy trying to make them see it in the light of Jean Anouilh's play, L'Alouette, which they are studying, to do much exploring myself,' she said ruefully.

'L'Alouette being about Jeanne d'Arc,' he supplied, and, as she lifted her eyebrows, went on, 'Yes, I have seen the play several times as a matter of fact, although I know you don't visualise me as a theatre-goer.'

'I hardly know how to visualise you, Nicolas,' she sighed.

'You're surprised to find that I appreciate the theatre, and literature. You think that *hommes d'affaires* only care for balance sheets and flow charts, and take-overs?' he enquired lightly, but with a faint frown.

'No. I now know you like messing about in boats, and scaling impossible cliffs, and demolishing plates of *fruits de mer*,' she said with matching levity, but knew as she spoke that she was no nearer the real heart of him. The core of the mystery still evaded her.

As they drove home later, he said, 'I have to be in Dieppe tomorrow. There is a meeting I can't get out of, but I shall be back in St Valery by evening. Have dinner with me?'

She looked at him gravely. All day he had made no attempt to touch her, although the reined-in desire to do so was almost palpable, and he must have been aware that she felt the same. Was he playing games with her? she puzzled, but somehow, deep inside her, she was convinced that he was not. In any event, she was in too far to say no, now.

'Seven-thirty,' he said, rightly taking her silence for consent. 'I'll book a table.'

The day was long and tedious without him. Julia walked on the cliff-top, she sunbathed, she pottered in the village centre doing desultory shopping, but all the time she could think of nothing but Nicolas, Nicolas. Her heart, her mind, and yes, her body, too, were measuring out the hours, the minutes, the seconds until the time she saw him again. She ached to be with him, and, more, she ached to touch him; he was becoming an unattainable grail she could not quite reach, ever just beyond her grasp and her understanding.

As seven-thirty approached, she spent a frenzied hour getting ready, showering until her skin tingled, and anointing herself liberally with creams and perfumes. Every article of clothing she had brought along was dragged out of the wardrobe and rejected several times before she sighed, gave up, and put on a simple white dress with a shirtwaist front. Her hair, of course, wouldn't do anything she asked of it, and in the end, in desperation, she scooped it up on top of her head and secured it with a knotted white chiffon scarf. She wanted him to go crazy at the sight of her, but she thought she looked awful, and couldn't see why he should. She hated herself for being this stereotypical female creature, frienziedly preparing and beautifying herself for male delectation, but she couldn't help herself. Nicolas Lestrille had put her beyond help. She did not know what to do about it, and by the time he knocked on her door she was a gibbering wreck of doubts and uncertainties.

She had seen the Mercedes arrive as she looked covertly through her window, watched him get out, crisp and immaculate in charcoal-grey trousers and a soft white shirt. Her eyes followed him hungrily across the quay to her door, marvelling that it had come to this, that she should find so much secretive delight in watching a man walk up to her doorstep.

Biting her lip fiercely, she made herself wait a full half-minute before she answered his summons.

The restaurant he had chosen, to Julia's surprise, was not in the town centre but a little way out along a pretty country road.

'I hope you don't object to a short stroll,' he said. 'I seem to have been in the car half the day, and I'm glad to get out of it.'

'Not at all,' she said politely, still strung up with concealed nervousness. 'It's such a lovely evening. Did your meeting go well?'

He pulled a face. 'I got what I wanted, although not without a struggle,' he said. 'Fortunately, I did not grow up expecting everything to come easily, which gives me an inbuilt advantage over those who did.'

The grim satisfaction in his voice took Julia back to the Nicolas she had first met in Dieppe, hard and peremptory, and as restful as a hungry tiger. But by the time they had reached their destination, some of the tension had left him, although there was still a sense of part of him having been left behind on the battlefield.

The restaurant was one which could have easily been missed, by anyone who did not know it. From the road, it looked like just another old grey Norman house, but at the back large windows opened out on to a wide terrace, with a half-wild informal garden beyond, at the far end of which a tethered goat contentedly munched the grass. Two cats stalked about as if they owned the place, eyeing the new arrivals with that superior disdain cats were masters of, and Julia gave a nervous little laugh. If tables had not been set out on the terrace and in the room beyond, she would have thought they had made a mistake and wandered into someone's back garden.

'The food is good,' Nicolas said humourously, noting her uncertainty. 'The *patronne* is charming, too. Shall we eat out on the terrace, since it's so warm?'

Several parties were already eating, but the tables were well spaced, and Julia felt very private, in a secluded corner with roses twining up trellises beside them. One of the cats came and sat under the table by her feet, and the presence of this purring, somnolent creature helped her to relax a little. She raised her eyes to look at Nicolas across the table, and found him looking at her with a quizzical smile on his lips, and a question in his eyes.

'Will you tell me something, Julia? Honestly?' he asked directly.

Startled, she said, 'Yes, if I can. What is it that you want to know?'

'Are you in a relationship with someone? I heard that you were—which is why I was surprised to find you here alone.'

She frowned. 'Who told you that?'

He shrugged. 'Does it matter? The grapevine. One hears these things around.'

She said, 'The grapevine is way out of date. There was someone, before I came to Dieppe with the exchange, but it was already over when I arrived in France.' After a slight pause, during which he said nothing, and seemed to be waiting for her to go on, she continued, 'He was another teacher at the college, but the thing went sour when I, and not he, was asked to do the exchange. In retrospect, I can't say I'm sorry.'

'And I can't say I blame you,' he agreed.

She moistened her lips. It was difficult, but she would never get a better subject-opener than this. 'Is that why...on the beach the other day...because you thought I had someone else...?'

He was silent for a few moments.

'Partly,' he admitted. 'Not altogether.' He toyed idly with the knife at the side of his plate, and she sensed him marshalling his thoughts. But in that very moment a woman came bustling out of the restaurant and gave a shriek of delight at the sight of him.

'Monsieur Lestrille—after so long! I thought you had deserted us!'

She was buxom and laughing, with red hair and mischievous eyes. Nicolas got to his feet and they exchanged the traditional French greeting of kisses on both cheeks.

'Pressure of work alone keeps me from your table,' he assured her. 'Julia, this is Madame Fleury, *la patronne*. Madame, this is my English friend, Mademoiselle Delaney, but don't talk about her in French, because she speaks it perfectly!'

'He would have you think I am a dreadful gossip!' said Madame Fleury, reproachfully. 'But I forgive him, and for you, *mes enfants*, only the best! Come along—order.'

Not until they were into their first course and relatively free from the delighted attentions of Madame Fleury, who loved to chat to her customers and seemed to have a soft spot for Nicolas, did he say, 'So you didn't stay in Normandy to get over a disappointing love-affair?'

She shook her head.

'No. I had planned on visiting my father, who lives in Bristol. He has a young second wife and two small children, and while they are not unwelcoming, I always feel...*de trop*. It happens every time I visit, and I keep hoping the novelty of their situation will have worn off, and I can be just a normal part of their family. But I was afraid it wouldn't be that way, so on an impulse I decided to stay in Normandy. I liked what I'd seen of it and wanted to see more, and being alone is better, anyhow, than not being wanted.'

She spoke lightly, but he must have heard the hurt in her voice.

'I'm sorry.' He laid his hand over hers, and Julia wondered if he could feel the pulse racing at his wrist. 'It can't be pleasant for you, but it's a sad fact of life that families can be difficult.

Well—I speak from experience. You already know a little about mine.'

'Only a very little,' she protested. 'You haven't told me what happened to your father after your brother helped himself to the château and your aunt Marguerite. Obviously that was not the end of the story, or you would not be here at all.'

She saw pain darken his eyes then, and feared she had overstepped the invisible mark, but he let go of her hand, poured more wine, and said quietly, 'My father died some years ago, but yes, you are right. What happened was that he quit Normandy for good, never to return, and went to live in Provence, where he met my mother and married her, and where, eventually, I was born.'

'But surely, that's a happy ending!' Julia insisted.

Nicolas shook his head.

'No, it wasn't,' he said soberly. 'The marriage wasn't happy. My mother was second best, and she knew it. All I can recall of my early years was their constant arguing, her weeping . . . doors banging . . . heavy silences. You know the sort of thing. Eventually, they divorced, but even that wasn't a great improvement. I become a kind of emotional football, to be tossed back and forth.'

'Oh, Nicolas, how awful!' Julia exclaimed with ready sympathy. She wanted to touch his hand again, but hardly dared, the current of bitterness floating from him was so strong it scared her. 'Is your mother still alive?'

'Yes.' He nodded. 'But I rarely see her. She went into some kind of enclosed religious retreat.

I never knew anything of my father's story until just before I left home to go to university, when she said she was virtually giving up the world, and there were things I had to know.'

Across the table, his eyes held hers, so directly that Julia could not move, and was almost afraid to breathe.

'My father was never happy out of Normandy. All his life, she told me, he had hankered after it, but he refused to go back—because of the château and the woman he could not have. Somehow, when I finished studying, I knew I had to seek out this side of my heritage, so I came to Dieppe, started out in business, and... well, you know the rest.'

'Became a tycoon,' Julia finished.

'It didn't happen overnight,' he said drily. 'But seeing the shambles Uncle Bertrand had made of the Lestrille estate certainly spurred me on.'

She understood, now, the driving force which had made him dedicate so many years single-mindedly to succeeding in life. Not only the need to make money to restore the château, which should have been his patrimony, but to vindicate the failure of his own father's dreams... to soar free of the shackles of his own miserable childhood.

'But it should have been your home... you should have grown up there,' she said.

'It isn't important where we start from,' he shrugged. 'The race isn't won at that end. It's what we make of ourselves that counts. If we have enough determination, enough ambition——' He broke off. 'Look—here comes Madame's celebrated *agneau pre-salé*. Let's do it justice.'

The lamb, grazed on salt marshes, was excellent, and so was the cheeseboard which followed. Julia, unable to choose between Neufchatel, Livarot and Pont L'Evecque, could not resist having a little of each.

'Not another mouthful could pass my lips!' she gasped afterwards, when he pressed her to try the dessert of apples, cream and Calvados. 'I couldn't possibly!'

'Yes, you can,' he insisted. 'Madame Fleury, bring us a *trou Normand*. Not,' he added quietly, 'the commercial stuff, but your special brew, you know?'

She winked.

'*D'accord*, Monsieur Lestrille,' she grinned, and came back with two tiny glasses of a colourless liquid.

'As you say in England...bottoms up!' said Nicolas, tossing down the contents of his glass in one mouthful. The wicked gleam in his eye should have warned Julia, but failed to, and she recklessly did the same. Her throat burned, her eyes watered, she coughed and spluttered helplessly, and then quickly drank half a tumblerful of the mineral water he poured for her.

Glaring reproachfully across the table at him, she gasped, 'What *was* that? Neat aviation fuel, or some such thing?'

He grinned.

'The *trou Normand* is an *eau de vie* distilled from the same apples that produce Calvados. It is supposed to clear one's palate between courses, so that in true Norman style one can digest vast meals. What we had was not, I assure you, what is kept on the bar shelves. It's a batch *madame* keeps for—er—privileged customers. Some old auntie of hers brews it down on the farm... illegally, of course... and the recipe will probably die with her.'

'Just as well!' Julia said hoarsely, her windpipe still scorched.

'But you are ready for a dessert, now, yes?' he said smugly, and she laughingly admitted that she was.

It was growing dark as they walked back after dinner; the lights had begun to refract and dissolve, glimmering in the black waters of the harbour. They walked close together, but not quite touching, and her awareness of him was so acute it was literally painful to her. The knowledge that she wanted him this badly took her breath away, and as they reached the door of the cottage she took a severe grip on herself as she turned towards him.

'Thank you for a delightful meal. I enjoyed it, in spite of being half choked,' she said, trying to dilute the intensity of her emotions in jest.

'Too much predictability is boring,' he replied. 'It is the unexpected which keeps us alive.' And then, almost as an afterthought, 'Aren't you going to invite me in—or do I have to make my own coffee on the boat?'

The unexpected, at this stage, temporarily stunned her. She had steeled herself for the polite goodnight, and the beginning of the long, tedious wait until she saw him again.

'No...that is, yes...come in,' she said, hiding her confused reaction by turning to open the door.

Inside, she switched on the lamp and was about to go through into the kitchen when he arrested her, placing both hands on her shoulders. Looking up into his eyes, she saw that they were very dark, and charged with intense feeling, and suddenly her own heart caught in her throat, like a snared and fluttering bird.

'Leave the coffee,' he ordered briefly, and gently but insistently drew her down on to the cretonne-covered couch and sat beside her, his hands still restraining her. 'You started to ask me something back there in the restaurant, and it hardly seemed the right moment to give you a proper answer. So here it is, now.'

One hand played lightly with the lapel of her dress, then moved to her throat, lightly grazing across her skin. Julia could not have moved if her life had depended on it.

'I did not make love to you, on the beach, for all I wanted to...as you must have known...not simply because I wasn't sure you were free. I don't think that alone would have stopped me, Julia, I'm afraid, not the way I felt...the way we *both* felt,' he corrected himself.

'What, then?' she whispered. 'Tell me, Nicolas. I didn't understand...and I want to.'

'The truth is that I don't trust relationships. Close, intimate ones, that is, where you have to give more of yourself than just your senses. Look what happened to my father, because he loved and trusted a woman. Look at my parents' marriage. I decided when I was very young never to allow myself to be hurt that way, and the sensible method of preventing that seemed simple to me— never get involved.'

'But you can't make love without getting involved,' Julia protested impulsively.

'*You* couldn't. I could see that. Your emotions are too deep, too intrinsic a part of you. But you stirred something in me the first time I met you. I tried to convince myself that it was only lust.'

'By being beastly and macho?' She lifted a hand and tentatively stroked his cheek.

'If you like.' He smiled. 'You kept on invading my thoughts, with your black hair and your contentious spirit, even after you had gone back to England.' Turning his face, he brushed the palm of her hand with his lips.

She gulped, all but beside herself with desire.

'And if you had not unexpectedly met me here in St Valery? We would never have met again,' she said.

'I think we would. The Channel is not that wide.' His hands moved into her hair, pulling loose the chiffon scarf and letting the black tresses fall free. 'We had to meet. This had to happen to me. I've gone through life making occasional love to women with my body only, giving nothing more. And now it's not enough. I want *you*, Julia. Not just your body—beautiful though it is—but *you*.'

Overcome by emotion, she murmured, 'Don't say anything more,' and as his mouth came down on hers her arms slid around his neck. His kiss was everything she had waited for—as firm and demanding as the first one, but now there was something else, an element of adoration, almost of reverence. She gave herself to it unreservedly, letting her body tell him that there was nothing, tonight, she was not willing to give. His fingers deftly undid the buttons down the front of her dress, and slowly, they slid to the floor together, wrapped in each other's arms.

The car's engine in the street barely touched Julia's consciousness, even when it pulled up outside with a vicious jerk of the handbrake. The slam of the door and the urgently running feet she could have ignored. But the sudden insistent rapping on the door brought them both to a swift, unwelcome recognition of the world beyond each other.

Nicolas raised his head and looked down into her eyes. His hair was ruffled, his shirt partly undone.

'Julia? Who is it likely to be at this hour? Whom do you know here?' he demanded in a low voice.

'I don't know...no one,' she whispered wretchedly, and they stared at each other like two guilty adulterers caught *in flagrante*.

The urgent knocking began again, and then a woman's voice called out, '*Nicolas? Tu es là?*'

'*Diable*! It's my aunt Marguerite!' he groaned, and swiftly tucked his shirt back into his trousers

and ran a hand through his hair. Julia, her fingers
leaden, somehow managed to fasten her dress and
compose herself, unable to escape the feeling that
she had suddenly been transported elsewhere and
set down in a strange dream.

Fortunately, Marguerite Lestrille, when Nicolas
admitted her, was too distraught herself to pay
much attention to their dishevelment. She cast
Julia only a fleeting glance and said, 'Oh...it's
Mademoiselle...'

'Delaney,' Julia supplied woodenly.

'That's right. I'm so sorry to burst in, but I
had not expected to find you here, and...' turning
back to her nephew '...I must talk to you,
Nicolas. In private,' she added pointedly. 'It's
about   Laurence—something   dreadful   has
happened.'

Julia got up at once.

'I'll make some coffee,' she said, and went into
the kitchen. She could hear the murmur of their
voices as she went about her task, Marguerite's
half-hysterical whisper, and Nicolas's quieter,
more placating tones. Some family crisis, she
supposed, and, for all she sympathised, she could
not help asking, why, oh, why had it had to
happen tonight, when, in the most marvellous
and unexpected way, she and Nicolas had been
on the verge of becoming lovers? When finally
she had broken through his reserve to the real
man behind it, and he had told her so much
of what motivated him, and how his life
had unfolded.

She carried the coffee tray through into the living-room, but Nicolas was already shrugging into his jacket.

'I have to go, Julia,' he said crisply, and the splendid romantic lover of ten minutes earlier had metamorphosed back into the efficient, purposeful individual she had first met, with no subtle shades of the transformation lingering between one and the other. 'Something has come up. Family problems.'

'I understand,' she said, and she did indeed understand why he felt he had to go, although not the reason for his swift, brusque reversal of personality. 'I do hope no one is ill.'

'No. Nothing like that,' he said, and that was obviously as much as he was prepared to tell her. 'Come along, Tante Marguerite. We'll take my car—I don't think you should be driving. I'll have someone come down and fetch yours.'

They were out of the door almost at once.

'Nicolas,' Julia called after him, and he looked back at her, frowning slightly, almost as if he had already forgotten her presence, when only a short time ago he had been holding her in his arms. 'When do you think you will be back?'

'I really can't say, Julia,' he replied distantly. 'I must go now, there's no sense in wasting time.'

She watched him settle his distracted aunt into the front seat of the Mercedes and slide behind the wheel. His face was taut and set as he started the engine, and he did not look back. When Nicolas Lestrille had a problem to solve, all his attentions were focused upon it.

Slowly, Julia closed the door and leaned back against it, letting out her breath in a long sigh. From the moment Marguerite had arrived, to the moment she and Nicolas left, events had moved with brutal swiftness, and she, Julia, had ceased to have any control over them, or any relevance. The miracle had, in a matter of minutes, turned into a nightmare.

It wasn't Nicolas's abrupt departure. She could have coped with that, if he had only held her hand briefly, or taken her aside and said, 'Look, Julia, I'm sorry I have to go, but there is a problem in the family. I'll be back again as soon as I can, and I'll be in touch.' She would not even have minded his not telling her what it was that demanded his immediate attention. All families had matters they kept among their own members, and his aunt obviously did not want to divulge this one.

No. What hurt was the feeling of being cut out, of being relegated to a lowly position of no importance. For all the desire and strong-running passion that had been carrying them both forward in its momentum to one inevitable end, he had deliberately and without too much effort switched off his emotions where she was concerned.

The room was just as it had been when they had come into it and fallen gloriously into one another's arms. Cruelly, it seemed, nothing had changed.

Except, when she looked down at the floor, there, lying on the carpet, crumpled and discarded, was the white chiffon scarf that she had worn in her hair, and which, with such splendid and empty symbolism, he had so recently removed.

CHAPTER EIGHT

BY MORNING, she had made all kinds of excuses
for his brusquely unfeeling behaviour. Clearly,
he had been worried. She had no idea what his
aunt had said to him while she was in the kitchen,
but it concerned his young cousin, Laurence, and
Julia knew he was fond of the girl.

Soon, she told herself, he would be back, and
in the light of the newly found trust which had
grown between them he would surely give her
some explanation of why he had had to leave with
such alacrity.

Then he would take her in his arms and kiss
her, long and thoroughly, as he had before, and,
at last, make love to her, as she was longing for
him to do. She melted inwardly at the mere
thought of it, and there was no longer any use
trying to ignore the torment of her body and her
emotions his absence was putting her through.

But the day passed, and he did not come back,
although she looked for his car every time she
heard one stop on the quayside. By ten o'clock
she had accepted that he would not be back today.

There was no telephone at the cottage, but
perhaps there would be a letter from him in the
morning, she thought as she went to bed. Surely
he could find a minute to scribble a brief note

saying all was well, and intimating when he expected to return.

Again, she was disappointed, and again the day went by with no word or sign of him. The next day, feeling slightly ashamed, she went into town to the estate agent's office, and asked, as casually as she could, if he had heard any word from Monsieur Lestrille.

But no, *mademoiselle*, the man had said, surprised by the question. Monsieur Lestrille turned up as and when it suited him. *Bien sûr*, his boat was moored here, but he needed no one's permission to come or go, and was not a man to have his movements questioned.

Julia left, feeling chastened and rather small. Clutching at straws, she had hoped Nicolas had phoned with a message, but he had not. Stopping by the public phones, she was seized by an awful temptation to phone Lestrille S.A. in Dieppe. Family crisis or not, Nicolas was Nicolas, and was sure to have touched base at his office. Even if he were not there, the trusty Etienne might have some information as to where he was.

She fought this temptation and conquered it, but only after a long, hard struggle. Where has your pride gone, Julia, she asked herself, walking home, that you should even consider attempting to track a man down in that way? How far down this road of need and desire she must have gone, to behave as she never would have dreamed of behaving before. But she had never felt like this before, had never been the helpless victim of such an irresistible passion.

She stayed on in St Valery for two more days, and by that time it had begun to dawn on her that Nicolas was not coming back. The moment that had stolen up on them that night had passed and gone, and was probably unrepeatable. Maybe he was already regretting the things he had said to her, the impulse to surrender to an involvement he had always vowed to avoid. Maybe he was thanking his lucky stars and his aunt's timely arrival for his narrow escape.

Toad! she thought disgustedly. Beast! How could he have led her to think he was sincere? 'We had to meet—this had to happen to me. I want *you*, Julia——' Ugh! She shook her head furiously, setting her dark locks tumbling around it. And there she had been, only too eager to fall into his arms and give him all she had, all she was. If she had, how could she be sure he would not instantly have cut and run before he had time to become more deeply involved?

Looking out at *La Liberté*, bobbing gently on the water, Julia straightened her back, lifted her shoulders defiantly, and came to a decision.

'Time and tide wait for no man, Nicolas, *mon ami*, and nor do I,' she said firmly, and went upstairs to pack her bags. Maybe she, too, had had a fortunate escape. She would forget him, get over him. She still had her career, and the rest of her life. She could not allow one man to ruin her entire existence.

She took the key back to the estate agent and looked sadly around at St Valery as she left. The boats still jostled together on the water; the flowers in the municipal beds were a bright symphony of reds and yellows. The shops and cafés bustled with people, and the air was keen with that fresh salt tang of sea and fish. Here, she had all but stumbled into the most passionate attachment she could imagine, with an improbable man who had excited, stimulated and often infuriated her, whose like she did not think she would find again.

Putting the car in gear, Julia drove determinedly away and up the coast towards Dieppe.

Nothing had changed in Merchester. The house was just as she had left it, apart from a light film of dust everywhere. The college was closed for the summer vacation, and would be for some weeks to come. She felt aimless, purposeless. In those few days with Nicolas she had lived a lifetime, and this gulf now separated her from the person she had been before she left for Normandy. The road back to that life, that woman, would be slow and difficult, and she would have to take it step by painful step.

First of all, the house. She spent a full day scrubbing, cleaning and polishing, throwing herself into these menial tasks with as much energy as she possessed, hoping that the effort would tire her out, and that she would sleep at night untroubled by thoughts of *him*. It wasn't a wildly successful ploy. She was exhausted, true, but exhaustion and sleep did not always go hand in hand, and she could not so easily drive him out of her mind.

Very well, she decided, if physical exertion didn't help, maybe mental endeavour was the answer. She would start on some preparation work for next term's classes. Her table was soon strewn with books, tapes, leaflets and newspaper articles to the point where she could scarcely find room to set down her coffee-cup.

The work got done, but it did not exorcise the memory of Nicolas, standing at the controls of *La Liberté*, the wind ruffling his hair, walking with her through the ancient streets of Rouen, taking her in his arms on a lonely beach.

She had to admit that she had lost—he had come close to her, then slipped away again. But when she remembered the look in his eyes, the throb in his voice, that last night in the cottage, her disobedient heart could not accept it.

I will—I must—I am not going to let this man get to me in this way, she told herself firmly. I will not allow myself to disintegrate, to fall to pieces because I can't have him, because he evidently decided he did not want me that much, after all.

She had been back three days, and the weather seemed set on echoing her mood of wretchedness. The glorious summer days had fled with her brief happiness, it was a dark, rainy, wind-tossed evening, and Julia was glad to draw the curtains and switch on the electric fire. Curled up in front of its comforting glow, in her pyjamas and dressing-gown, she sipped her coffee and contemplated an early night. She probably wouldn't sleep, but there was little incentive to stay up, either.

The shrilling of the doorbell roused her to a startled alertness. It was not yet ten o'clock, but hardly a time for casual, uninvited callers. She had, anyhow, deliberately avoided people since her return. She did not feel ready, as yet, to put on a smiling face and pick up the social reins.

The bell shrilled again, and Julia fastened her dressing-gown around her and peered out of the window, but it was too dark and miserable to discern anything more than the form of a man under the shadow of the porch. She opened the door a little, slipping on the chain. She was not over-cautious by nature, but any woman who lived alone had to take a modicum of care.

'*Tiens*, Julia, are you going to leave me standing here getting wetter and colder by the minute?' Nicolas demanded irritably. 'Open the door properly and let me in, and stop being stupid!'

She gaped at him, astonishment rendering her motionless. The Mercedes was parked by the kerb, and in the short space between there and the door, his hair had indeed been soaked in rain. He was wearing a short black leather jacket over black jeans, and there was something demoni-acal about his appearance, compounded by the angry glitter in his eyes, dark grey in the light which escaped from the entrance hall.

'I don't *want* to let you in, and I have no intention of doing so!' she exclaimed sharply, and made to shut the door in his face. He forestalled her by swiftly planting his foot firmly in the aperture.

'It's raining, in case you had not noticed,' he stated coldly. 'And it's late. What do you expect me to do?'

'There are plenty of hotels,' she retorted. 'And since I don't know why you are here, what has it to do with me?'

'It has everything to do with you. I did not turn you away when you crossed the Channel to see me, and at the very least you could have the courtesy to return the compliment. Now——' Since she had not moved, he reached a hand past her and, releasing the chain, pushed open the door.

'Of all the nerve—how dare you?' she blustered, but he was inside now, the door closed behind him, and there was little she could do about it. He was large and powerful and angry, although why the latter she could not fathom, since he was the one who had gone off and left her without a word.

Turning, she stalked furiously into the living-room, but it was not an escape route, as he merely followed her, shrugging off the leather jacket and slinging it on to a chair.

'I dare very easily. I'm not used to being treated in such a cavalier fashion!' he declared roughly. 'Is that the way you usually behave towards your. . . friends? Running off and deserting them the minute they have a problem that prevents them dancing attendance on you? Huh?'

He took her by the shoulders and shook her, lightly but contemptuously, as though she were no more than a rag doll.

'Get your hands off me!' she demanded. 'I won't be bullied like this—by you or anyone else.'

'I shall do exactly as I please,' he said ominously. 'You were only too willing to have my hands on you on our last encounter, I seem to recall. Anywhere I wanted to put them was fine by you.'

She flushed dark with humiliation.

'Maybe I behaved like an idiot that once, but I'm not usually so foolish!' she flung back at him. 'I'm not proud of it, and you can be sure it won't happen again!'

'We'll see about that,' he said, and his eyes echoed the veiled threat in his voice. 'Meanwhile, I'm still waiting for an answer. Why did you run out on me?'

She gasped incredulously.

'I waited several days, Nicolas, during which time you neither came back, nor wrote, nor sent me even the briefest message of what to expect!' she cried accusingly. 'You simply walked out and abandoned me as if I had ceased to exist. What was I supposed to do?'

'You could have tried a little patience,' he said harshly. 'You could have trusted me a little. After all, I thought we had reached...an understanding.'

'Oh, yes,' she replied bitterly, 'we had! I understood perfectly. You expected me to sit around indefinitely, while you came and went as it suited you, until you finally decided whether you wanted me or not. To hell with that, Nicolas! No man's going to keep me on a string like that!'

He narrowed the distance between them, backing her against the wall.

'That's all you think about, isn't it? Your own all-important self-image, how liberated you are, or appear to be,' he sneered. 'It hasn't even occurred to you to ask about my problems, not once since I came through the door!'

She strained away from him, but the wall was flat and hard against her back, and his threatening body only inches away from her vulnerable, thinly covered flesh.

'You've hardly given me the chance!' she protested defensively. 'Considering the amount of secrecy you and your aunt were intent on maintaining, I doubt you would want to tell me anything!'

'That is not the point,' he said, with slow, heavy emphasis on each word, laying his palms flat against the wall either side of her, so that she was effectively imprisoned.

'I think you had better leave,' she said, in a voice that trembled slightly.

'I'll leave when I am ready to,' he said. 'First of all, we have some unfinished business, and I think you know what it is.'

A swift hand loosened the belt of her robe, and with a sharp tug pulled the garment from her. Julia gasped, but now she was free to move she found she no longer had any desire to do so. Excitement was suddenly running through her like a tide that could not be turned back. The thinly controlled violence in him, the anger, scared her, and yet she was shaking with an exhilaration not born of fear, and she did not resist as he lowered her to the ground, and unbuttoned the jacket of her pyjamas. Already, her own hands were working their way inside his shirt, and the shock of contact as their naked skin came together made her cry out.

'Tell me to get my hands off you, now,' he said, in a voice thick with complacency. '*Alors*— go on—say it! If you can!'

She could not. She could hardly wait for them to get out of the rest of their clothes, to touch him and hold him to her, to feel his hands and his mouth exploring her. For all his anger and impatience, he proved a subtle and skilful lover, drawing out every ounce of response in her, making her wait in order to thrill her all the more, and at last, when she thought she could stand it no longer, and begged him to finish, taking her to an ecstatic climax.

She buried her face in his shoulder, still shaking, and full of a deep, barely understood astonishment. It made no difference that he had come to her in a furious, punitive mood, that he had handled her roughly and spoken to her with scathing contempt. It made no difference that he still had not explained his absence, and seemed unlikely to. He had turned up out of the blue and simply taken her, and even though she had argued with him and insisted he leave he had known she wanted him, and behaved accordingly. She was

his now, in every fibre of her being, and knew
it, and he knew it too.

His skin was suddenly damp with tears she was
fighting not to shed, and his hand stroked her
hair with unexpected tenderness.

'I did not intend to be rough with you, *petite*,'
he said quietly.

'You weren't. It's not that——' she said shakily.
'It's just that I never expected to feel like this.'

'Nor I,' he said simply. He sat up, drawing her
up with him and looking deep into her eyes,
smiling a small, puzzled, rueful smile. 'No—
that's a lie. I knew it would be like this with you,
Julia. I knew we would make the world explode
if we came together. That's why I resisted it as
long as I could, but I couldn't keep away from
you. I'm a marked man.'

He rubbed the back of his neck and grinned
wryly. 'In more ways than one. You have sharp
claws.'

'You asked for it,' she retorted, with a sudden
recovery of spirit.

'Indeed I did. And I will again.' He stretched.
'But not on the floor, I hope? You do have a
bed, I take it? And something to drink would not
go amiss.'

What she did not have was a man's dressing-
gown or any other kind of masculine garment,
so they sat in front of the fire, she in her loosely
fastened robe, he with a blanket draped round
him like a toga, thirstily disposing of the bottle
of wine she had opened.

'So tell me,' she ventured, 'is everything all right now with your aunt and your cousin Laurence.'

'Not exactly. But I'm working on it,' he replied. 'I'm sorry, Julia, I really can't tell you any more than that.'

Once again, the pain of exclusion stabbed at her, briefly, but she shrugged it off. Perhaps it didn't really matter. Nicolas was here with her, his arm round her shoulder, his lips warm against her hair, and whatever had happened, *he* had come in search of *her*. He would not have done that if he had had no feeling for her.

She turned towards him curiously.

'Just how did you manage to find me?'

He laughed.

'That was easy. Any number of people in Dieppe who were concerned with the exchange have your address, Olivier Gérard to name but one. A street guide did the rest.' He drained the last of the wine from his glass. 'Julia. Let's go to bed. I want to make love to you again—this time in comfort.'

It occurred to her briefly that he had taken for granted he would stay the night. But, presumptuous or not, he was right. She wanted him in her arms all night, wanted to wake and find him there in the morning. There was no point in denying it now.

Some time in the small hours of the night, she stirred from a heavy sleep to find her whole body aching for him again. Instinctively, he was awake too, and impatient to possess her. With the barriers of inhibition lowered by her half-conscious state, she found herself reaching new heights of abandon, giving and taking with a sensuality she had only half suspected she was capable of. And then she slept again, as if loving and sleeping were part of one long continuous dream.

It was the rattle of cups which brought her to the surface once more, and she opened her eyes to find Nicolas, clad in no more than his navy silk boxer shorts, setting the tray on the bedside table.

'Wake up, *paresseuse*—lazy thing,' he admonished. 'I have been in your kitchen, making tea, while you were oblivious to everything.'

'Tea?' She blinked and stretched, then pulled the sheet back over her nakedness.

'It is a bit late for modesty such as that, is it not?' he grinned, and Julia blushed, remembering the marvellous excesses of the night. Surely she could not really have behaved with such incredible abandon? But his lasciviously amused smile assured her that indeed she had.

'Did you find everything—in the kitchen, I mean?' she muttered, pink-faced.

'I did, although you English never have any camomile tea, or other infusion, only this stuff.' He made a Gallic moue of distaste. 'Unfortunately, I drew the blinds to see if it had stopped raining—which it has—and gave your postman rather a shock as he came up the path.'

Julia groaned theatrically.

'I'm a ruined woman,' she said with heavily feigned reproof. 'Don't you realise that I have a respectable position in the community, and a reputation to maintain hereabouts?'

'Not any longer, you don't,' he said cheerfully. 'Is there a decent bakery anywhere nearby, where I can get some croissants for breakfast?'

'Gracious, nothing like that!' she scoffed. 'First thing in the morning? This is England, *mon cher*! You will have to settle for toast and marmalade!' She smiled in happy anticipation of the day ahead. 'Then I'll show you the town. We have a splended ruined castle your Conqueror built, right next door. Or would you rather have a brisk walk on the Downs, and lunch in a pub?'

He laid a cautionary hand on her arm, and she saw that his face had clouded over slightly.

'I can't stay, Julia, unfortunately,' he said. 'I have to go back to France.'

Her blue eyes were wide with disappointment and disbelief.

'Today?' she demanded incredulously.

'Right away. On the ten o'clock ferry,' he admitted. 'This thing with Laurence—I told you, there are still matters to be dealt with.'

'And they can only be dealt with by you?' she asked heatedly. 'What about her father—your uncle Bertrand?'

He shook his head contemptuously.

'He can only make matters worse. I am the only one she trusts,' he said. 'I must not let her down.'

Julia's cup rattled in the saucer as she set it down none too gently.

'And what about me?' she asked. 'Don't I count for anything?'

'*Bien sûr*,' he said levelly. 'I am here, am I not? I should not have come away, leaving everything still unsettled, but I did.'

'Thank you,' she said with heavy sarcasm. 'Thank you for sparing one night for me, Nicolas, out of your tight schedule. I am supposed to be overcome with gratitude, am I?'

'But what a night,' he said. He drew the sheet down to her waist, smiling a slow smile as he looked her over, then he leaned over and kissed her lips, her throat, then her breasts. She felt the unquenchable tide of desire rising in her once more, and knew that any minute now he would be making love to her yet again, thinking that if he did she would be quiescent and accepting, that he could silence all her arguments, dispel all her doubts, simply by taking her in his arms? But surely, that was not enough.

Julia sprang out of bed, dragging the sheet with her.

'If you're itching to do your disappearing act, don't let me keep you!' she said frostily, and headed for the bathroom without a backward glance.

When she came back, he was no longer in the bedroom. She dressed quickly, brushed her tangled hair into obedience, then went downstairs.

She found him fully dressed, spruce and immaculate, a world away from the splendid lover in her bed. Why did he have to be these two separate people? she wondered resentfully. All her actions were sharp and ill-tempered as she busied herself making toast, and more tea, she felt tight-lipped and close to tears.

'You are making an unnecessarily big deal out of this,' he told her, and the clipped tone of his voice reduced her to the status of a petulant fourth-former being told off by the class teacher. 'I have family business to take care of, it is as simple as that. And I don't care for anyone—*anyone*—trying to confine me and question my motives.'

'Far be it from me,' she said loftily. 'You are a free agent, Nicolas, and can go wherever you want, when you want. You've made it clear that your family problems are none of my concern. But don't get attached to the idea that my bed is here for you to leap in and out of whenever you feel so inclined.'

He raised his head and regarded her levelly.

'*Ah, bon*,' he said. 'If I merely wanted a bed to leap into, I did not have to travel this far. There are beds nearer home.'

'Oh, I'm sure of it,' she said. 'A breezy Channel crossing first merely adds piquancy to the act.'

He scraped back his chair, his face taut with disdainful annoyance.

'I don't have to put up with this,' he said contemptuously. Then in an instant, the lines around his mouth softened just a little, he came round the table, and, taking Julia's face firmly between his hands, bent and kissed her—long, hard and possessively, squeezing the breath out of her, pre-empting any resistance she might have offered.

'I think it is best I go now,' he said, when at last he released her, leaving her shaken and bereft of speech. 'There are things I must do, but then, there always are and always will be, and if you can't accept that, Julia, then I am the wrong man for you. I suggest you think about it.'

At the door, he turned.

'*A bientôt*,' he said simply, and then he left.

Julia stood at the window with clenched hands, watching him walk down the path and get into the Mercedes. Every instinct in her was screaming at her to run after him and throw herself into his arms, to prevent him from leaving her in this coldly angry mood, but she did nothing. Her eyes followed the back of his proud head, then the tail-lights of his car as it cruised down the hill and turned finally from sight at the bottom.

Last night, she had given herself to him as fully and completely as it was possible to do. She now belonged to him utterly, in every way. Maybe his abrupt departure, his stubborn lack of any real lack of explanation, were hard to take, but did they give her the right to behave like a jealous teenager with her first romance?

Julia turned away from the window, shivering slightly, although the sun was shining. She knew, really—of course she did—why she could no longer control her own tempestuous emotions, why she had been unable to take a firm grip on herself and act reasonably. Why, this very minute, she ached to have Nicolas back in her life and in her arms, and why even an hour of separation seemed, to her, too long.

It was because she loved him. What else?

CHAPTER NINE

IN THE days that followed, Julia thought long and
hard about those few hours with Nicolas, and
her own realisation that she was in love with him.
Not that she doubted her conviction for a minute.
She had never in her life known such a fierce and
passionate involvement, and it did not begin and
end with the pleasure they had shared in bed—
although the mere thought of that was enough
to set her heart racing painfully.

Did he love her too? That was the question
that troubled her mind. She was convinced that
he desired her, more than any of the women to
whom he had admitted making 'occasional' love.
But his determination to exclude her from other
aspects of his life disturbed her, for what was
love, if not a sharing of each other's fortunes
and misfortunes?

She would have to let him come to her when
he was ready, she decided. Childhood experience
had left him with a lingering mistrust of relationships, a reluctance to commit himself. If, instead
of questioning and haranguing him as she had
done the last time they were together, she de-
monstrated her trust in him, and simply waited
until he had sorted out his problems at home,
perhaps he could be persuaded of the real

strength of her feelings, and be able to return
them in kind.

But as time passed and he did not contact her,
this splendid resolve began to falter. He was doing
it again, she realised, absenting himself as it
suited him, and it was then she began to think
more seriously about some of the things he had
said before he left.

I don't care for anyone trying to confine
me...if you can't accept that, Julia, then I am
the wrong man for you...

Maybe he had already worked out for himself
that they were incompatible, she with her im-
portunate emotionalism, he with his innate, deep-
seated reserve. He had probably weighed up the
pros and cons and decided not to come back to
her, not to get in touch with her again.

After all those ecstatic hours in each other's
arms, could he simply turn his back on the heights
of pleasure they had enjoyed? There were beds
nearer home, he had said prosaically, and, if they
did not provide him with the same ecstasy,
perhaps there was less hassle involved in sharing
them.

I am not going to phone him, she thought
grimly, gritting her teeth. Loving him was her
misfortune, and it was in her very nature, when
she loved, to hold back nothing. That was what
she had done, and, if he did not realise it or value
the significance of her commitment to him, there
was nothing she could do. It was hard, very hard,
and a hundred times a day she reached for the

phone and then drew back her hand. If he cared for her at all, the first move now must be his.

But when the telephone did ring, and she snatched it up, hoping eagerly that it would be him, the voice she heard was that of Anne-Sophie Duval.

'I thought perhaps I should get in touch with you to discuss the second half of the exchange,' the French girl said.

'Already?' Julia was surprised. 'But we are only halfway through the vacation. Don't you think it's a little early?'

'Oh, well, maybe it is.' Anne-Sophie appeared to relinquish her intention readily enough. 'I shall talk to you about it again, a little later. Did you enjoy your holiday, by the way? I heard that you stayed on in Normandy, although you had not told me of your intention.'

'That's because I didn't know myself, until the last minute. It was pure impulse,' Julia replied guiltily, wondering if Anne-Sophie was capable of understanding such a concept. They had not achieved the kind of rapport which would have encouraged Julia to visit her while she was there, and she rather imagined the other girl was well aware of this. Furthermore, she wondered how Anne-Sophie had even learned that she had been there at all.

'Oh, well—*tant pis*. So long as you had a good time. One hears that you have been seeing something of Nicolas Lestrille.'

'My goodness,' Julia said mildly, her voice deliberately casual, 'it amazes me how these snippets of information fly back and forth across the Channel! Yes, I did run into him, quite by chance, as it happened.'

'Ah.' Anne-Sophie's pause was short, but meaningful. 'Forgive me if I seem to be interfering, but I should warn you to be careful there.'

'I don't really think it is anyone's concern but my own,' Julia said, trying to remain polite while holding down a rising irritation. Anne-Sophie wanted to tell her something, of that she was sure, but she was not at all sure she wanted to hear it.

'You must not take offence so easily,' Anne-Sophie reproved her in her rather priggish manner. 'I was only trying to warn you against becoming too much involved. *Le tout Normandie* knows that Nicolas is going to marry his cousin, Laurence—and I think it will be soon.'

A frozen horror rooted Julia to the spot, and for a moment her brain cells cut out; she could neither speak nor think. But then, feeling crept back into them, and she reasoned—Anne-Sophie was only talking. It was just gossip. How could she know this? And how could Nicolas have said all the things he had said to her, made love to her as passionately as he had, if he was planning to marry another girl?

'I think that has to be pure speculation,' she said levelly. 'Nicolas is very fond of Laurence, but I've no reason to believe that he is in love with her.'

Anne-Sophie's laugh trilled out in astonishment at Julia's naïveté.

'Oh, *ma chérie*, maybe he is not,' she agreed smugly. 'But he will marry her nonetheless; it is an understood thing. Bertrand and Marguerite de Lestrille have no son to inherit the château, which in any event should belong to Nicolas by right. Marriage to Laurence will tidy up all the loose ends neatly, you understand?'

Julia did not want to believe any of this, and she fought a fierce little battle against doing so. But into her mind kept drifting odd snatches of memory—Nicolas striding into his uncle's château as if he already owned it, talking about his father's loss with such bitterness in his voice. And there was all the money he had spent on the restoration. It was hardly surprising that he should feel the château should be his, and marriage to Laurence would finally make it so. He would have come home, and his own children would grow up there. But still...

'People don't marry for that kind of reason these days, Anne-Sophie,' she said practically. 'Not without love.'

'Believe me, in such families as this, they still do,' the French girl contradicted her. 'Besides, there must be some affection, as you said yourself. Laurence is young, but she and Nicolas have always been close.' She paused again dramatically, and then threw her best shot into the game. 'I am sure they will marry, and I think it must be soon, they have no choice. Because of the baby.'

The baby?

The telephone table, the bowl of flowers standing on it, the garden in her view outside the window, all merged and swam before Julia's eyes, and she leaned a hand on the wall to steady herself.

'Laurence is going to have a baby?'

'Oh, yes. No one is supposed to know that, of course. But these things have a way of getting around, do they not?' Anne-Sophie's voice was replete with the satisfaction of one who has unwelcome news to impart. She never liked me, Julia thought, but did she have to take quite so much pleasure in the telling? 'That's why I advised you to take care,' she went on patronisingly. 'Of course, if she has any sense, Laurence will not object to Nicolas's having the odd affair now and then. It's natural for a man such as him, is it not?'

'I think you are being presumptuous, and I have heard enough!' Julia exclaimed, her control suddenly snapping. 'It's nothing to me whom Nicolas Lestrille marries, and I don't know where you got the notion we were anything other than casual acquaintances. Goodbye!'

She slammed down the phone and stood shivering with delayed shock. She was going to have to talk to Anne-Sophie again before long; indeed, when the exchange got under way next term, she was going to have to co-operate with her. It was not going to be pleasant.

She did not care. Right now, all she could think of was Nicolas, and the utter duplicity with which he had behaved, letting her think he was falling in love with her, when all the time he was planning to marry Laurence. Julia was modern enough to accept that nowadays all love affairs did not lead to marriage, but what he and Laurence had was tantamount to an engagement, and he should not have pursued and embarked on a relationship with Julia while he was not truly free.

She saw it all, now, pieced it together neatly for herself. Marriage to Laurence was meant to be at some future date, perhaps when the girl was a little older. Meanwhile, he considered himself at liberty to dabble in as many affairs as he chose, and his time allowed. Involvement with her had got a bit out of hand, perhaps; he had found himself more strongly attracted than he had bargained for. She had pierced his shell. But he had still deceived her, implicitly if not directly.

The whole fabric of his neatly structured plan had come apart when Laurence had unexpectedly become pregnant, and the marriage needed to be brought forward. Hence Marguerite's night-time dash to St Valery, and Nicolas's reluctance to explain his absences. A wedding was being arranged, and between the arrangements he had found time to whip across the Channel and stake his claim firmly on Julia before she found out. Believing, no doubt, that once they had so ecstatically become lovers she would be unable to give him up, and he could pick up the relationship at will, after his marriage.

Julia swallowed hard. She felt sick—sick at heart, and literally, physically nauseous. Those

sunlit days they had spent together in St Valery,
getting to know one another, days when the spell
of him had been weaving its magic around
her... and further back than that, when she had
first met him, and fought his savage attraction... all that time, he had been making love
to someone else. She wanted to hate him; maybe,
in a sense, she did hate him, but, unfairly, the
hatred did not kill her love, or her continuing
desire.

If he were to walk in now, and take her in his
arms, what would she do? He was *not* going to
get through her door if he stood out there all
night, Julia vowed, and if he phoned she would
tell him to go straight to hell. She would never,
ever let herself be in a situation where she might
be tempted to pick up where they had left off.
She had no intention of being Nicolas Lestrille's
bit on the side, the English *petite amie* he kept
discreetly tucked away this side of La Manche!

That afternoon, she had to get out of the
house. The claustrophobic sensation of its four
walls was driving her mad, but at the same time
she did not want to go out in Merchester where
she was sure to run into someone she knew. In
the end, in desperation, she got into her car and
drove to Brighton.

The day was fine and sunny, and the town was
chock-a-block with tourists and shoppers. Julia
wandered aimlessly around the Lanes, determined to do some shopping but in no mood to
find anything that took her fancy. The maze of
little streets behind the seafront was thronged

with people, gazing in the windows of the many boutiques and jewellers' shops, sitting at pavement tables outside cafés and pubs. She dived into a dark, chic little dress shop to escape the crowd, and bought an expensive dress she did not really want, and was sure she would not like when she got it home. Sighing, she turned into a sunny, sheltered square and made for her favourite café to seek solace in a cup of tea.

It wasn't true. It wasn't fair. Sitting outside at a table, the sun gilding his hair, his legs comfortably crossed, was Nicolas.

Julia stopped dead in her tracks. He was not alone; his arm rested along the back of his companion's chair, he was talking to her intently, and it had to be Laurence.

Julia would have known her if she had bumped into her in the street, for she was quite simply a younger version of Marguerite. The same tumbling cascade of blonde curls, the same heart-rendingly lovely face and slender body. Her pregnancy obviously was in its early days, for she was reed-slim in her jeans and a lacy summer top which emphasised her firm young body.

She could not move. Nicolas, she thought wretchedly, makes love to this beautiful creature. Everything he has done with me, he has also done with her, and she is going to have *his* baby. She could not bear it. She wanted desperately to turn and run, but she could not persuade her leaden limbs to obey her, and after a few seconds, as was bound to happen, he glanced up and saw her.

'Julia,' he said with a calm smile. 'We really must stop running into one another so coincidentally.'

'I shop here often,' she said. 'It's you who are off your beaten track.'

'The Channel can be crossed in either direction.' He directed his smile back to the girl at his side. 'This is my cousin, Laurence. Laurence, this is Julia Delaney.'

She had a lovely smile, Julia had to admit.

'Ah, yes,' she said, her face candid and open. 'Nicolas has spoken of you.'

'He has?' Julia wondered faintly what on earth he could have told her. She risked a glance at him, but his expression betrayed not a tremor of guilt or apprehension. Well, what had she expected? He was presumably too experienced a player in this sort of game to be disconcerted by the meeting of two women he had taken to bed. The memory of that night came rushing back to her in a hot flood of shame and desire, and for a moment she thought her knees would give way.

'Join us for the wonderful English institution of afternoon tea,' Nicolas suggested, clicking his fingers to summon the waitress. 'I shall order a fresh pot, and more scones with jam, although Laurence here is making a poor effort at eating hers.'

'I can't,' she said, pulling a face, and, looking up at Julia, she confessed, 'I don't feel too well.'

'I'm so sorry,' Julia said stiffly. The girl did look a little pale, and she knew from the horror stories with which Rosie had gleefully regaled her that the first months of pregnancy were not easy. 'I hope you will soon feel better. Don't order anything for me, Nicolas, thank you. I have to go—my parking voucher is running out.'

And with that, she did at last manage to turn and hurry back, bumping apologetically into people in her haste to get away, reaching, at last, the sanctuary of her parked car, where she sat with her head on the wheel and sobbed shamelessly.

A tap on the window alerted her, and she looked up fearfully, but it was only a concerned-looking policeman.

'You all right, lady?'

She sniffed and wiped her hand across her eyes, smudging her mascara.

'Yes thank you, Constable, I'm fine. Bit of a headache, that's all. I'm on my way, now.'

He was still watching her doubtfully, so, with a tremendous effort of will and concentration, Julia turned the key in the ignition, eased out of the parking space, and drove off in the busy flow of traffic along the seafront.

Merely surviving what remained of that day cost Julia more reserves of strength and endurance than she had thought she possessed. She couldn't face the possibility of seeing or talking to anyone, so she locked her door firmly behind her and took the phone off the hook. Eating anything was out of the question, so was indulging in any kind of normal human activity, such as reading a book, or watching other people communicating with one another on the television screen. She was cut off from all that, existing in a tight, pain-lapped little capsule all on her own, set well apart from the rest of humanity. As soon as it was decently plausible to do so, she crawled into bed, pulled the duvet over her head, and lay stiff and unmoving until dawn crept through the window.

After a cup of tea and two bites out of a slice of toast that tasted as inviting as cardboard, she reluctantly replaced the telephone receiver, and no sooner had she done so than it shrilled into the waiting silence. Julia watched it for a while, willing it to stop, for whoever it was to give up the attempt to get through to her, then, as it still went on insistently ringing, she picked it up, and leadenly said, 'Hello.'

'Julia?' It was Nicolas, sounding outraged and irritated. 'What's going on? I've been trying to get through to you since I got back to Dieppe, and I'm assured your telephone is not out of order.'

'There was no need for you to phone me,' she said, wishing that he would ring off, while still, perversely, loving the sound of his voice with its faint, intriguing acccent.

'Well, of course there was,' he contradicted impatiently. 'I needed to speak to you. I have something I want to tell you, and it's important.'

Panic caught her by the throat. He was going to tell her about Laurence and the baby and his impending marriage, knowing that she was bound to hear about it soon, anyway. But she did not want to hear it so finally and definitely from his own lips. She did not want to hear him admitting that another girl was going to have his baby, and was to be his wife.

'No, Nicolas,' she said sharply. 'I don't want to talk to *you*.' Grasping at any reason she could find, she went on quickly, 'Remember before you left, you said I should think seriously about... about us? Well, I have, and I agree that we are not right for each other.'

'You thought we were, that night we spent together,' he said wryly. 'Have you forgotten that?'

How could she have forgotten? How could she ever forget the way she had felt when they had made love? But she was not about to leave the door open so that he could come back to her after a decent interval. She did not want to be a married man's lover. It would not be fair on Laurence or herself. Maybe Laurence could accept it, as Anne-Sophie had hinted. Maybe the French saw such things from an entirely different viewpoint. But Julia could not cope with such a relationship. She wanted love, not just occasional sex, however exciting.

'Oh, that,' she said, with forced dismissiveness. 'It's very easy, isn't it?'

'Is it?' he challenged. 'You think everyone is automatically given what we had? If so, you are severely mistaken, Julia. And if you think you are going to feel that way so *easily* with someone else, then there again I fear you are deceiving yourself.'

'Modest as ever, Nicolas,' she murmured sardonically.

'*Mais non*. Just honest,' he replied. 'And you will admit it yourself, if you have the courage to be the same.'

All this was meaningless, Julia thought desperately, and unless she managed to end this conversation she would be drawn inevitably into telling him she already knew about Laurence. She might even end up revealing how much he had hurt her, and how much she loved him, and she could not bear to make such an abject exit from his life.

'Perhaps. But there has to be more than that, for me, at least,' she said. 'What happened between us was just one of those quick-flash physical attraction things. Fun, but ephemeral. So, no hard feelings, but ... *au revoir*.'

She put down the phone again and stood by it for a full minute, waiting to see if he would ring back again, but there was only silence. Did he believe her? Had he accepted that whatever they had had was over? He was not a man to accept defeat easily, but nor was he one accustomed to chasing after a woman.

His businessman's instinct might well tell him that in sexual encounters, as in corporate affairs, there were times when one must persist and times to cut one's losses, and this was one of the latter. He was getting married soon, he had a large organisation to run, and how much valuable time could he afford to waste over a woman who was playing hard to get, a little late in the day. He had already had her, fully and comprehensively, and, for all he might have enjoyed repeating the experience, there would be other women, no doubt.

However he had reasoned it out for himself, he did not call her again, either on that day or during the days that followed, and Julia wondered miserably what was worse—her fear that he might try to contact her again, or her growing certainty that he had indeed decided that enough was enough. With the passing of the days, the second explanation became more and more likely, and she dragged herself through the week barely able to concentrate on anything.

When the phone next rang, it was her father, calling from Bristol, telling her cheerfully that Rosie was pregnant again.

'Goodness, that was quick,' Julia said faintly. She had had enough news of imminent births for one week.

'Well, I'm not getting any younger, girl, and I don't want to be seeing my kids through the school gates then toddling off to collect my pension,' said Liam.

'You're nowhere near that stage!' Julia laughed, vainly picturing her handsome, youthful-looking parent as a senior citizen.

'I suppose not.' She could almost visualise him proudly preening himself. 'Anyhow, Rosie wants a big family.'

'Well, congratulations. Give everyone my love,' Julia said. I might have quite liked the odd sibling myself, she thought, with just a twinge of bitterness. But Liam had been too obsessed with his career then, and hadn't wanted to be bogged down with babies!

Men! she mused resentfully. Why did they have to have everything their way all the time, as and when it suited them? Her father, Adam, Nicolas—oh, especially Nicolas? They all thought the world was created for their sakes, made and designed for their pleasure.

I'm through with them all, thought Julia defiantly, and then she looked a little way into the future, and saw herself becoming like Anne-Sophie Duval—prim, repressed, existing vicariously through gossip about other people, and she shuddered. She would rather be like Miss Scott: firm, no-nonsense, understanding but with all that behind her.

But she was not going to effect an overnight transformation from herself to Miss Scott. That would take years of struggle and self-denial, of being alone, and accepting being alone as a way of life. And it could be, she thought soberly, with a flash of insight, that even for Miss Scott the solo state had not been a matter of choice, simply never the right man at the right time... or the demand of too great a sacrifice.

Julia looked deep into her own soul, her own psyche, and knew she was not the stuff lone women were made of, for all she had ambition and dedication aplenty. There was too strong a need in her for love, emotional and physical. Having known both, she craved and longed for them, but the awful, tragic truth was that they both came clothed in the persona of Nicolas Lestrille, the man who had fathered another woman's child, and would soon be her husband.

CHAPTER TEN

SHE had not believed that black week could hold anything worse, but on the Friday morning she had another telephone call from Dieppe, this time from Olivier Gérard.

Unlike Anne-Sophie who, Julia was convinced, had telephoned only to crow, Olivier really did have genuine queries about the second leg of the exchange trip, and Julia spent some time discussing the requirements of his students on English soil, and his progress in finding local employers around Merchester to provide them with work experience.

'It all seems to be falling into place,' she said, and could not help remembering that chilly spring day when she had crossed the Channel to confront Nicolas in his office. It seemed so long ago—although it really wasn't—and she had learned so much about herself since then.

'If my arrangements go as smoothly as yours did, my dear girl, I shall be more than happy,' he said. 'As I recall, there was only one small mishap, and you dealt with it compassionately and speedily. Of course, you had Nicolas to help you, which was fortunate.'

Even the sound of his name on someone else's lips was enough to start a sick, thumping sensation around her heart.

'Yes, he was very efficient,' Julia agreed woodenly.

'Speaking of Nicolas,' Olivier continued jauntily, 'have you been invited to the Lestrille wedding, by any chance?'

'No...no, I haven't,' Julia said, her free hand gripping the edge of the telephone table as if she might collapse without its support. 'I did hear something about it, though. Is it...is it to be very soon?'

'Soon? Why, it's tomorrow, dear girl.' He sounded surprised that she did not know. 'I thought perhaps Nicolas would have...well, never mind. It is to be at the church in the village near the château, at twelve-thirty. Why don't you pop over and see the ceremony? It will be a grand event, I understand. My wife and I will be there, although we are not going to the reception at the château. You would be welcome to stay with us overnight.'

'Oh...you're too kind...but really, I couldn't,' Julia forced out the words. There was a painful obstruction somewhere in her throat, and her voice, even her breath, fought their way past it only with the greatest difficulty.

Tomorrow? *That* soon? But of course, with the baby on the way, they would want the marriage celebrated as soon as possible. Marguerite, from the state she had been in that night in St Valery, was obviously anxious to have the proprieties observed and a not too visibly *enceinte* bride at the altar, no matter how casual the spirit of the age was about such things. And Nicolas? Well, married or single, he would live his life exactly as he chose to, Julia reflected bitterly.

No wonder he had wanted to speak to her, she thought, to tell her that he was getting married, and quickly. And close on this realisation came another. Big weddings were not arranged overnight, and Nicolas must have known this was in the offing, the night he had come storming furiously into her house, making love to her with such savage intensity. He was, already at that time, a man with his wedding date fixed on the calendar.

'I'm sorry... I can't come, but thank you very much, all the same,' she heard herself repeating, then made some excuse about having a hairdressing appointment in ten minutes' time. Anything to get away from this subject and this conversation, as quickly as possible!

That night there was to be live New Orleans jazz at one of the local pubs, and several of Julia's friends were going along. Julia loved jazz, and although she had not committed herself to being there, thinking that she would not be able to endure the lively atmosphere and the company of other people intent on enjoying themselves, as evening approached a feverish, reckless mood began to invade her gloom.

So she could not exactly dance at his wedding to prove she couldn't care less, but there was nothing to stop her going out, meeting friends, and having as good a time as she could manage. Or, at least, giving the appearance of having a good time. Nicolas, of course, would not see her or know what she was doing, and none of her friends here knew about her affair with him, so this little exhibition would be for herself alone. To boost her terminally depressed morale, and prove to herself, that, at twenty-five, her life was not over on account of one man.

She ran herself a long hot bath, washed her hair, and spent a lot of time getting dressed up in a mode that was casually glamorous—loose, shining hair, long, swinging earrings, a fluffy red sweater embroidered with beads over her best, most figure-flattering jeans. And she was rewarded for her effort by the relief and pleasure of her friends in seeing her back on the circuit.

'You've been so generally unavailable this summer, word was you'd either died or emigrated,' someone said, and she smiled her most winning smile, even though it was forced.

'No, I'm here, and still in the land of the living,' she said, accepting the glass of wine thrust into her hand.

'And looking sexier and more enticing than ever, if I may say so!'

It was Adam, deeply tanned and just back from his holiday in Florida.

'Well, thank you,' she said, pleasantly but quite coolly. Flattery was always acceptable and at the moment more so than ever, but he needn't think his compliment sent her over the moon!

The air was hot and smoky; the music, seductive as cream, tore at the heart, with words that echoed all that lovers had ever felt. Adam sidled up to Julia and offered her another drink, sliding his arm around her shoulder.

'I mean it, Julia. You look terrific,' he said. 'What have you been doing to yourself in my absence?'

I've been falling in love, she thought, refusing the drink and evading his arm. The touch of any other man but Nicolas left her cold, and the slight, monochromatic feeling she had once had for this one was now no more than an unappetising memory.

He, however, seemed impervious to her lack of enthusiasm for his attentions.

'You know, you really upset me over that exchange business, but I'm willing to let bygones be bygones, and give you another chance,' he said magnanimously.

Julia's mouth pursed in a small 'O' of astonishment, and then she was hard put not to burst into stinging laughter. He had to be kidding? But no, his face was quite serious, and he clearly thought he was doing her a tremendous favour.

'The only thing upset was your ego,' she said mildly. 'As for the idea of there being anything between us again—well, no, Adam, I'm not interested.'

She turned away, then, seeing another friend she wanted to talk to, and glad of the excuse but not before she noted the nonplussed expression on his face. A flicker of genuine amusement crept into the false gaiety of her mood as she realised he could not bring himself to accept she was no longer attracted to him at all.

Nicolas had not believed it, either, but not because he was an egocentric fool like Adam. Nicolas had known the fullest and deepest extent of her passion, had felt her unfailing response every time he touched her. He was right—she was not over him, and probably never would be.

Suddenly alone in the crowded, noisy, smoke- and talk-filled bar, Julia experienced a moment of revelation. This was all pretence. The reality was that across the water in Normandy, at twelve-thirty tomorrow, Nicolas was getting married. But it would not be real to her unless she saw it, unless she had, with her own eyes, visible evidence that he belonged to another woman. In that moment, she knew she had to be there and to see him for herself, or she would never, ever be able to put her love for him behind her, and pick up more than the trappings of her former life.

The heat swirled, trapped beneath the low ceiling, the chatter died away, and the band began to play 'Ain't Misbehavin',' the beat smooth and insistent, the lyric delivered with a wry, throaty intensity. Julia smiled, waved goodbye, and under cover of the music, slipped out into the cool air of the street. She had a boat to catch at seven in the morning.

Of all the days Julia had prayed the ferry would depart dead on time, on that fateful occasion it chose to leave Newhaven fifteen minutes late.

'Something to do with the tides, they say,' she heard one of her fellow passengers mutter to his companion.

Tides might still be something over which man had no control, but Julia hoped the boat would make up the time and arrive in Dieppe as scheduled. It was a four-hour crossing, and with the hour's time difference that would make it midday at the earliest before they reached France, then she had to disembark, which could take a while, and find a way of transporting herself to where the wedding would be taking place. It would have to be a taxi. Expensive, but she could not risk the delay of enquiring into public transport which might be scarce or inconvenient. Unless she made it in time to see him, the whole exercise was pointless.

Which it probably was, anyhow, she thought, sitting in the lounge bar and toying with a cup of coffee, which was all she could face. Some of last night's inspirational mood had faded with the daylight, and although she still believed in her mission, still thought the only hope of exorcising the spirit of Nicolas from her heart was by actually seeing him with his new bride, as the moment approached she viewed it more in the nature of an ordeal—like sitting one's finals, taking one's driving test and visiting the dentist all in the same day!

The journey seemed interminable, a trip into an unending purgatory. She watched as Beachy Head drifted past the windows, and the English coast faded from sight behind them, and then there was a long stretch with nothing but rolling waves and the occasional passing trawler to divert her. She took herself to the bar and ordered a brandy, for all it was only ten in the morning, and sat sipping it slowly to steady her nerves.

Then, at last, the Normandy coast came into view, white cliffs and green fields under a pure china-blue sky; the port of Dieppe was a blur of walls and buildings, which gradually materialised into identifiable landmarks as the ferry drew nearer, and edged neatly into its berth almost at the heart of the picturesque town.

It was twelve-fifteen as she emerged from the Customs shed and traversed the footbridge to the quay, and finding a taxi took her a further five minutes. She did not know the name of the church or of the village in which it was situated, but could only describe it as being close to the château owned by the Lestrille family. But that was sufficient for the driver, who nodded sagely.

'*Vite, s'il vous plaît,*' Julia urged him.

It was easily said, but less simple to achieve. Saturday was market day, which meant that Dieppe was full of shoppers and vehicles, and several roads were closed in addition to the normally pedestrianised areas. They hit a traffic jam almost at once, and she had to sit biting her nails as they edged forward, inches at a time, always held up by traffic-lights that changed to red just as they reached them.

Cursing under his breath, the driver took a roundabout route to get them clear, and at last they left the city behind them. Julia, looking at her watch for the fiftieth time, saw that twelve-thirty was already in the past.

She sat back in her seat, suddenly deflated, as if all the effort had gone out of her. Did it matter that the wedding would already be under way? She was not here to interrupt at that vital stage when the congregation was asked if there were any known impediment to the union. She had not planned to leap up, shouting, 'No—she can't have him! *I* love him!'

In fact, she thought, as the taxi left the main road and chugged along the country lanes heavy with overhanging greenery, it was better if she did not actually go into the church itself, but waited outside for the couple and their entourage to emerge. The last thing she wanted was that Nicolas should see *her*, and this would be more easily prevented if she hung about in the church yard, preferably on the fringe of the spectators who always seemed to turn up for a wedding, like extras for a film set. Then she could simply watch as they came out, and quietly melt away again, unnoticed.

Would it serve any purpose? Now she was almost there, she had begun to suspect that she would feel worse, rather than better, as a result of seeing him, but at least, whatever happened, it would make it real. She would have no choice other than to accept it as done, and her own part in the story as finished.

The village, when they reached it, was tiny, and silent as the grave, with that hush which descended on French villages when the sacred hour of *déjeuner* arrived, and the shops closed their shutters until later in the afternoon. And today, especially, there was no one around because, as Julia realised the moment the taxi drew up outside the pretty stone-built church, everyone was here. It must be full inside with invited guests, and all those who had simply come to watch were standing around in the church yard.

'Would you please wait for me when you have found somewhere to park?' Julia asked the driver. 'I shall be wanting to go back to Dieppe in a short while.'

He pulled the taxi over to the other side of the road, alongside the line of waiting guests' cars, and Julia made her way unobtrusively into the church yard, taking up a position well to the rear of the throng. She was smartly dressed in a cream jersey dress and matching jacket, but fortunately nothing flamboyant which would draw attention to her, and no one paid her any notice as she stood quietly waiting.

The service would be well in progress now, she reckoned, looking up at the sky above the squat stone belltower, where rooks wheeled and cawed noisily. Only her gloved hands, twisting one with the other, betrayed the nervous tension almost tearing her apart from within. The faint breeze stirred a tendril of black hair across her cheek, and she brushed it back, wishing that this would soon be over.

Suddenly, a rustle of anticipation ran through the waiting spectators, and in a peal of music, the church doors were flung open. There was a soft, communal murmur of 'Ah——' and right then Julia would have given ten years of her life to be anywhere else on earth. She had been totally insane to come here, voluntarily subjecting herself to this anguish, but it was too late now, for here they came, the newly united couple.

Laurence was radiant in a billowing confection of ivory silk and lace, all her pallor gone, her cheeks pink, her eyes sparkling. She stepped out proudly, clinging to the arm of a young man Julia had never seen before in her life, but into whose face she gazed up with utter adoration. He bent his head towards hers to kiss her lips as the guests spilled out of the church behind them.

Julia could do nothing but stand stock-still where she was, like a statue carved in stone. The church tower, the quarrelsome rooks, the murmuring, laughing crowd, all spun around her, and she reached out and caught hold of the one solid object she could find, the twisted trunk of an ancient yew tree.

Had the world gone mad? This wasn't Nicolas with Laurence! Even as she stood transfixed, she saw him emerge from the church with Bertrand and Marguerite, looking splendid in his grey morning suit, and smiling with quiet satisfaction.

The crowd in the church yard shifted, surging forward to get a better glimpse of the nuptial pair, but Julia remained where she was, exposed and alone, and all at once highly visible; over the moving bodies and swaying hats, over the laughter and chat and the popping of flashbulbs, Nicolas looked straight at her, and he, too, was momentarily rendered motionless with palpable surprise written all over his face.

But only for a moment, and then she saw him whisper something in Laurence's ear, and set off towards her, easing his way through the throng.

She turned in a panic. She did not understand what was happening, but a blind instinct told her she should not be here, and must get away, and she began to run, awkwardly in her pencil skirt and high heels, out of the churchyard and down the lane towards the waiting taxi.

She was no match for his long, swift stride, and he caught her up well before she reached it, seizing her by the shoulders and spinning her round.

'Julia—Julia, I thought I had to be dreaming!' he said, and his voice was hoarse with emotion. 'I couldn't believe it was really you!'

She stared up at him, feeling the hard, much wanted pressure of his fingers, and her eyes misted over.

'I came to see you married,' she said in a low, puzzled voice.

'Me? Are you crazy?' he exclaimed incredulously. 'It is Laurence who is now married, as you saw.'

'Yes, I know that.' Her voice came only with great effort. 'But I thought...I thought she was marrying you!'

He frowned, displeasure flitting across his face. 'What? Who told you that nonsense?' he demanded peremptorily.

'Well...Olivier Gérard...' she mumbled. 'He...he asked me if...' She searched for the words, trying to call back precisely what Olivier had said. 'He asked me if I were going to the Lestrille wedding.'

Nicolas shrugged, unimpressed.

'So? This *is* the Lestrille wedding,' he conceded. 'No doubt that is how people are referring to it, although Laurence now has a new name. But my only part in it was to act as best man to the groom. I don't see how you could possibly have misunderstood to that extent.'

Julia's face was a study of incomprehension.

'But there's the baby...' she faltered.

'Yes, and Laurence is now married to the baby's father,' he said patiently, and then suddenly he let her go, and banged one fist down hard in the palm of his other hand. 'Julia...*mon Dieu*, you didn't think that *I* was he?' He looked deeply and questioningly into her eyes. 'After everything that had happened between *us*? Besides, Laurence is more like a young sister to me than anything else!'

With an abrupt, decisive movement, he took her arm, not roughly, but firmly.

'You and I have to talk,' he said in a tone that did not envisage refusal. 'Is this your taxi? I'll pay him off.'

He did not let go of her arm as he fished in his pocket and handed the puzzled taxi driver an exorbitant pile of notes before sending him back to Dieppe. Then he led her to where the white Mercedes was parked.

Julia glanced nervously across at the churchyard where chatting and photo-taking was still in full swing.

'But...the wedding...you're supposed to be there...'

'I've done my stint,' he said. 'Get in the car, Julia.'

She had thought they were only going to sit and talk, but he started the engine and eased away. As they cruised along the country lanes, he said, 'This is what Marguerite came to see me about in St Valery, and what I could not tell you, then or later. Laurence had fallen in love with a young man who was over in Brighton, studying English at a language school—that's why you saw us there. She had found out that she was going to have a baby, and they were keen to marry, but...the boy was not Bertrand and Marguerite's choice. Marguerite made me swear not to tell a soul until the problem was sorted out. To her, it was a disgrace, although, *bien sûr*, it is not at all unusual these days.'

Julia, still in a daze, said, 'So what did you do?'

He gave a slight, dismissive shrug.

'Mediated—what else could I do? Talked to all the parties separately, and together, and got them talking to each other. In the end, Bertrand and Marguerite had to accept Laurence's choice with reasonable grace, and a wedding was arranged.'

'If only I had known all this!' Julia murmured.

'I hoped you would trust me, *chérie*,' he said with a grave smile.

'I tried,' she protested. 'I wanted to. If only...if only...' She hesitated, reluctant to name names. 'If only other people had not interfered.'

He turned the car off the road, and Julia, who had hitherto been oblivious to the route they were taking, saw now that he had pulled up outside the old manor house by the stream, where they had stopped and talked on their very first day out.

'Remember this place?' he asked her.

Julia nodded dumbly. She was numb with apprehension that he was going to tell her, now, that her lack of confidence in him had destroyed their blossoming relationship—that she herself had spoiled it. But he got out of the car and held out a hand to lead her over to the fence.

'You did not learn about Laurence's baby from Olivier Gérard,' he said quietly. 'He did not know about that. Very few people did.'

'But I thought it was the talk of Dieppe——' she burst out, and looking at him, caught the knowing expression on his face.

'Your thoughts were deliberately poisoned, *ma petite*,' he said gently, 'and I think I know how. It was Anne-Sophie Duval who told you all this, was it not?'

Julia was silent for a moment, but seeing that he knew, anyhow, whispered, 'But how did she know? And why did she want me to get a false impression?'

He smiled, a strange, self-parodying smile.

'As for the first question, she has a relative who works at the château. And she makes it her business to find out every little thing she can about me. You may put this down to what you call my habitual lack of modesty, if you wish, but I have to be truthful. That woman—Anne-Sophie—has had a fixation about me for years. I hardly know her, but she thinks she and I are predestined soulmates who must some day come together. She told me so once, at a cocktail party, and I pretended to think she was tipsy, but eventually I had to accept that she was entirely serious, in a crazy way.'

'She's in love with you?' Julia gasped.

'If you will. In so far as anyone can be in love with someone they don't really know. I would call it more of an unhealthy obsession.'

Julia was remembering, now, all the comments Anne-Sophie had made about Nicolas, right from the beginning. In fact, almost every erroneous prejudice she had taken on board concerning him had come from that source, from her insistence that he had no interest beyond business, and merely used women as light relief, to her final announcement that he was to marry his cousin and was the father of her child.

'She must have known I would find out the real facts sooner or later,' Julia said. 'The Channel is not that wide.'

'Obsessive people rarely think reasonably,' he said, and now he had both her hands tightly in his. 'You were getting a little too close for comfort, my love.'

Her gasp was more pleasure than pain. '*What* did you call me?'

'My love. *Mon amour*. Have it in which language you choose,' he said fiercely. 'Either way, you must know I love you, Julia. You must have known after we were together that I would not have let you go.' He raised her hands to his lips and kissed both of them. 'Now either tell me you love me too, or tell me I am a complete idiot, for if I have read this wrong I must be.'

Her arms slipped round his neck. 'You are not wrong,' she said huskily. 'I love you. Unbearably. Crazily.' And lifting her face, she eagerly sought his kiss, delighting in it.

He kissed her mouth, her throat, his hands sliding down her back to mould her to him.

'I can't believe this is true!' she sighed. 'It made so much sense, what Anne-Sophie said, that if you married Laurence, the château would belong to you, as it always should have.'

'It was what Marguerite wanted,' he confessed. 'But as I told you, Laurence is more like my kid sister. Neither of us is in love with the other. Both of us are in love with someone else.'

His arm tightened around her shoulder.

'I don't want that blasted château, Julia,' he said firmly. 'It means nothing but ancient sorrows to me. Laurence and her husband are welcome to it. I have other plans. Let me show you something.'

He pulled from his pocket a ferry ticket which he handed to Julia.

'You will see that I was booked on the five-thirty sailing tonight—as soon as I was decently able to escape from the wedding festivities.'

Another document followed, a thicker one, which he had to unfold to show to her. Julia looked at it, and then at him, complete confusion in her blue eyes.

'It's a deed to a house!' she exclaimed. 'But... my name is on it!'

He nodded. 'And mine, too. This is the house.' He pointed at the manor house, dreaming tranquilly beside its stream. 'It's empty now, Julia, since I made the previous owners an offer they couldn't refuse. I want us to live there together. When we are married, *sans doute*! You do like it, don't you?'

Julia began to laugh, happy, excited laughter, tempered by a wry understanding of this man she loved, who did nothing by halves, in whose vocabulary the word 'failure' was not allowed to exist.

'This is all too fast for me, but yes, and yes again!' she cried. 'I love the house, and you, and... yes, I'll marry you! But, Nicolas, *mon amour*, what *would* you have done if I had said no, and you had already put the house in my name?'

He grinned.

'You don't succeed in any venture by admitting the possibility of failing,' he said. 'I would have camped outside your door until you gave in. At the very least, you would have been part owner of a property which would have drawn you back to Normandy again and again. I didn't see how I could lose. Do you?'

She was in his arms again, laughing and crying at the same time.

'No, my love,' she said. 'I don't see how either of us can. Not now—not ever.'

She put her arms round his neck as he lifted her over the fence and set her down. Then, vaulting it lightly, he took her hand, and they set off together to explore their new kingdom.

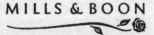

Next Month's Romances

Each month you can choose from a wide variety of romance with Mills & Boon. Below are the new titles to look out for next month, why not ask either Mills & Boon Reader Service or your Newsagent to reserve you a copy of the titles you want to buy – just tick the titles you would like and either post to Reader Service or take it to any Newsagent and ask them to order your books.

Please save me the following titles:		Please tick	✓
THE SULTAN'S FAVOURITE	Helen Brooks		
INFAMOUS BARGAIN	Daphne Clair		
A TRUSTING HEART	Helena Dawson		
MISSISSIPPI MOONLIGHT	Angela Devine		
TIGER EYES	Robyn Donald		
COVER STORY	Jane Donnelly		
LEAP OF FAITH	Rachel Elliot		
EVIDENCE OF SIN	Catherine George		
THE DAMARIS WOMAN	Grace Green		
LORD OF THE MANOR	Stephanie Howard		
INHERITANCE	Shirley Kemp		
PASSION'S PREY	Rebecca King		
DYING FOR YOU	Charlotte Lamb		
NORAH	Debbie Macomber		
PASSION BECOMES YOU	Michelle Reid		
SHADOW PLAY	Sally Wentworth		

If you would like to order these books in addition to your regular subscription from Mills & Boon Reader Service please send £1.90 per title to: Mills & Boon Reader Service, Freepost, P.O. Box 236, Croydon, Surrey, CR9 9EL, quote your Subscriber No:..................................... (if applicable) and complete the name and address details below. Alternatively, these books are available from many local Newsagents including W H Smith, J Menzies, Martins and other paperback stockists from 12 August 1994.

Name:..

Address:..

....Post Code:........................

To Retailer: If you would like to stock M&B books please contact your regular book/magazine wholesaler for details.

You may be mailed with offers from other reputable companies as a result of this application. If you would rather not take advantage of these opportunities please tick box. ☐